Rabbit Tales

Rabbit Tales

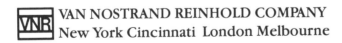

Barbara Purchase

A Nicholson Press Book

VNR VAN NOSTRAND REINHOLD COMPANY
New York Cincinnati London Melbourne

To Mitchell Temkin and Mary Corcoran for their invaluable assistance and guidance

Copyright © 1982 by The Nicholson Press
Library of Congress Catalog Card Number
81-16255
ISBN 0-442-24530-0

Printed in the United States of America

Design/Maher & Murtagh

Published in 1982 by Van Nostrand Reinhold
Company
135 West 50th Street
New York, New York 10020, U.S.A.

16 15 14 13 12 11 10 9 8 7 6 5 4 3 2 1

**Library of Congress Cataloging in Publication
Data**
Main entry under title:
Rabbit tales.
1. Rabbits – Literary collections. 2. Rabbits –
Addresses, essays, lectures. I. Purchase, Barbara.
PN6071.R2R3   808.8′036   81-16255
ISBN 0-442-24530-0   AACR2
ISBN 0-442-24529-7 (pbk.)

The editor wishes to thank the following sources for kind
permission to include the following illustrations in this
book:
Chapter One
The Albertina, Vienna, for "The Hare" (detail) by Albert
Durer.
The Cooper-Bridgeman Library, London for #4965: "Stray
Rabbits" (1858) by Robert Collinson, courtesy of the Vic-
toria and Albert Museum;
#6643: Needlework picture embroidered in silk on wol-
len canvas; English, circa 1720, courtesy the Victoria and
Albert Museum.
The Ann Ronan Picture Library, London for #3550: "Hare
Pursued by Hounds," from *Le Voleur*, Paris, 3 March 1876;

#134/87: "Boy With Pet Rabbits," from William Howitt,
The Boy's Country Book, London 1839;
#201/3/198: "Rabbits (lepus cuniculus)" from *The Royal
Natural History*, Frederick Warne & Co., London (circa
1855);
#55/68: "A Hare" from Thomas Bewick, *Select Fables*,
Newcastle, 1820;
#3547: Rabbits and Young (Lepus cuniculus)" and "Hares
and a Levert (Lepus europeus)" from *The Penny Maga-
zine*, London 23 October 1841.
Insel Verlag, Frankfurt am Main, for "Ich hore was, was du
nicht siehst," by Almust Gernhardt and Robert Gernhardt
© 1975 by Insel Verlag.
Lepus Variabilis Pall. hybridus
Chapter Two
Methuen & Co. Ltd., London, for an illustration by Ernest
H. Shepard from "Rabbit's Busy Day," from *The House at
Pooh Corner* by A. A. Milne, published 1928.
Houghton Mifflin, Boston, for an illustration by A. B. Frost
from *Uncle Remus and His Friends* by Joel Chandler
Harris, published 1892.
Ann Ronan Picture Library, London, for #224/93, "The
Hare and the Frogs," illustration by Gustave Doré from
The Fables of La Fontaine, London, 1867.
Tenniel's illustrations of the White Rabbit from *Alice's
Adventures in Wonderland* by Lewis Carroll, circa 1865.
Illustration to "The Rabbit's Bride" from *Grimm's Fairy
Tales*.
Chapter Three
Jonathan Cape, for "The Valley of Peace" by Wayne Ander-
son, from *Ratsmagic*, © 1974.
Nature Magazine, April 1935, for "How the Rabbit Stole
the Otter's Coat" from A Cherokee Indian Myth retold by
Dorothy Pletcher.
Ann Ronan Picture Library, London for #3551: "End of the
Hare Season" from *Punch*, London 22 March 1884;
#1856/rev/b: "A Rabbit Drive in California" from *The Pic-
ture* Magazine, 1894;
#224/665: "The Rabbits to the Duke of Rochefoucauld:
Gustave Dore's illustration for *The Fables of La Fontaine*,
London, 1867.
De Lepore
Andreae Alciati: Cum Larvis non luctandum
Emblema CLIIII
Chapter Four
W & R Chambers Ltd., London for "Cowper and his Pet
Hair," from *More Animal Stories*, by Robert Cochrane.
Michael Holford Photography, London for "A Hare Hierog-
lyph, the Symbol of Unnefer, painting from the coffin of
Ankhefenkhons A Priest." After 1000 BC. British Museum.
Ann Ronan Picture Library, London for # agr/st/4: "A rab-
bit warren – Thetford, Norfolk," from the Rev. Isaac Taylor,
Scenes off British Wealth, London, 1790.
#85/369 and #85/374: "Hare" and "Rabbits" from
Thomas Bewick, *A General History of Quadrupeds*, New-
castle, 1790.

#01/195: "Mountain Hare in winter coat," from The Royal Natural History, Frederick Warne & Co., London c1885. "De Quadrupedibus," from Gesner, Konrad; *Historia Animalium*.

Chapter Five
Cooper Bridgeman Library, London for #2991: Raeburn, "Boy and Rabbit," Royal Academy, London; #9303: "Pets" by G. Sheridan Knowles; A&F Pears Ltd. Ann Ronan Picture Library, London for #3549: "Hare coursing," from *Rural Scenes*, Harvey & Darton, London, 1825; #104: "Woman Selling Rabbits," from William Henry Pyne *Costumes of Great Britain*, London, 1808. #131: "Various uses of the hare and the rabbit," from a lithograph circa 1840.

Chapter Six
Bethnal Green Museum, for "Rabbit Ninepins," felt and wool, English, late 19th century.
Cooper Bridgeman Library, London, for #9860: "Rabbits," Victorian Easter card, Private collection; #9297: "More Watership Down," by Fred Morgan, A&F Pears Ltd.
Ann Ronan Library, London #3549: "Hare Coursing," from *Rural Scenes*, Harvey & Darton, London, 1825.
The Metropolitan Museum of Art, New York, Hewitt Fund for Franco Flemish Tapestry © 1500.
Illustration to "The Rabbit's Bride" from *Grimm's Fairy Tales*.

Appendix
Artist's Cards, London for "Head of Hare," © Pete Kettle. The Thomas Fisher Rare Book Library, University of Toronto, for 15 plates from *Die Saugthiere in Abbildungen nach der Natur mit Beschreibungen* by Johann von Screber, Erlangen berlegts Wolfgang Walther, 1792 Every effort has been made to ensure that permissions for all material were obtained. Those sources not formally acknowledged here will be included in all future editions of this book.

The editor wishes to thank the following sources for kind permission to include textual excerpts in this book: D. Appleton and Company, New York for "How Mr. Rabbit Lost His Fine Bushy Tail" from *Uncle Remus, His Songs and His Sayings* by Joel Chandler Harris, 1920; Avon Books, New York and Andre Deutsch Limited, London for selections from *The Private Life of The Rabbit* by R. M. Lockley, 1974; Elizabeth Coatsworth for "Song of the Rabbits Outside a Tavern" from *Rainbow in The Sky* ed. by Louis Untermeyer, Harcourt Brace Jovanovich 1941; Curtis Brown Limited, New York for "Jack Rabbit" from *Heroes Advise Us* by Adrien Stoutenberg; E. P. Dutton, New York and McClelland & Stewart Ltd., Toronto for "Rabbit Has a Busy Day" from *The House at Pooh Corner* by A. A. Milne, copyright 1928; William B. Erdmans Publishing Co. for "Nine Rabbits" by John Frederic Bennett from *Echoes From the Peaceable Kingdom*; Faber and Faber Limited for "A Birth Story of Buddha" from *The Leaping Hare* by George Ewart Evans and David Thomson; Gage Publishing Limited for "Peter Rabbit" by Dennis Lee, copyright 1974 by Dennis Lee; Harper & Row, Publishers, Inc. for "The Jackass Rabbit" and "A Plague of Rabbits" by Mark Twain from *The Higher Animals: A Mark Twain Bestiary* ed. by Maxwell Geisman; Eleanor Heady for "How The Hare Learned to Swim" from *Tales of East Africa*, Follet 1972; Houghton Mifflin Company for a selection from "Annus Mirabilus" from *The Poetical Works of John Dryden* ed. by George R. Noyes 1909; and for an excerpt from *Walden* by Henry David Thoreau; The Literary Trustees of Walter de la Mare and The Society of Authors as their representative for "March Hares" from *The Complete Poems of Walter de la Mare*; The Loeb Classical Library for selections from *Aristotle: Historia Animalium* and *Aelian: On The Characteristics of Animals*; *Nature Magazine* for "How The Rabbit Stole The Otter's Coat: A Cherokee Indian Myth" retold by Dorothy E. Pletcher, April 1935; Oxford University Press for "Epitaph on a Hare" from *The Poetical Works of William Cowper* ed. H. S. Milford; McIntosh and Ottis Inc. for "Molly Cottontail" from *The Complete Stories of Erskine Caldwell*; Random House Inc. for "A Rabbit as King of The Ghosts" by Wallace Stevens from *The Complete Poems of Wallace Stevens* and for "The Hare and the Hedgehog" from *The Complete Grimm's Fairy Tales*; Rex Collings Ltd. for a selection from *Watership Down* by Richard Adams; Richard Rieu for "The White Rabbit" by E. V. Rieu from *The Flattered Flying Fish* published by Methuen & Co.; Louise H. Sclove for "A Rabbit Parable" by Arthur Guiterman from *Wildwood Fables* Stakpole Books for "Rabbit and the Moon Man" from *North American Indian Folktales* by Allan A. McFarlan; The Scarecrow Press Inc. for "The Rabbit's Foot" by Joseph O. Clarke from *Beastly Folklore* 1968; T. F. H. Publications for selections from *Rabbits* ed. by Paul Paradise; Mrs. James Thurber for "The Rabbits Who Caused All The Trouble" and "The Tortoise and The Hare," copyright 1940 James Thurber, copyright 1968 Helen Thurber from *Fables For Our Time*, published by Harper & Row, Publishers, Inc.; Brian Swann for "When" from *To See The World Afresh* compiled by Lilian Moore and Judith Thurman, Atheneum Publishers, New York, 1974; University of Tennessee Press for "Divine or Degraded" by Beryl Rowland from *Animals With Human Faces* 1964; Viking Penguin for "The Hare and The Frogs" from *The Fables of LaFontaine* trans. by Marianne Moore, 1969; Frederick Warne & Co. Ltd. for "Beatrix Potter's Pets" from *The Art of Beatrix Potter*; A. P. Watt Limited for "Let There be Lettuce" from *Spirits of The Corn and The Wild* by J. G. Frazer 1912; Viking Penguin Inc. for "Bismark, The Demoniacal Rabbit" from *Women in Love* by D. H. Lawrence, copyright 1920, 1922 D. H. Lawrence, renewed 1948, 1950 by Frieda Lawrence; John Weatherhill Inc. for "Why Rabbits Jump" from *Nursery Rhymes From Japan* ed. by Charlotte de Forest, 1967.

CONTENTS

The first real rabbit I remember seeing was caught in crossed shafts of moonlight and car headlights, petrified, like a pale stone statue, on a country road. I asked my father, who had brought our station wagon to a screeching halt only a few feet from the animal, why it didn't run away and was told about its distressing tendency to freeze rather than flee when overwhelmed with fear. It was also explained to me, because I wondered where the creature's owner was, that the rabbit (and its cousin the hare) isn't a farm animal. Nor is it a common house pet. And it's not what one would call "wild," in that, unlike a wolf or a bear, for instance, it's cuddly, sweet-faced and relatively harmless. As I came to appreciate years later, rabbits and hares exist in a twilight world when it comes to behavioral classification—they live in cities as well as in rural and wild areas; they're easy to breed and care for as pets, and yet they cope successfully, and more or less harmoniously with humans, when left to their own devices.

I date my fascination with rabbits from that evening over twenty-five years ago. By the time I was eight I was already aware of one major difference between rabbits and hares (hares have longer ears), which was no mean accomplishment considering that most people consistently mix up the two animals. My scant knowledge of lagomorphs was proudly imparted to a group of school friends who were attending my eighth birthday party and who, during a backyard game of hide-and-seek, discovered a nest of six newly born, fawn-colored hares (not rabbits I insisted, probably falsely) in our garden. Under the supervision of my mother, who was as surprised as we were at our find, we children were allowed to gently pet the huddled clumps of fur. They were no bigger than our small hands, and their quick heartbeats seemed to rack their tiny bodies like sobs. The next day, to my immense disappointment, the nest was gone. Either the mother, upon returning to her brood, had picked up our human

scent and redistributed her leverets, or a cat or dog had come upon the nest during the night. I fervently hoped the former event had taken place but refrained from searching for the hares and easing my mind in case I drove the mother to flee again.

One might logically surmise from the foregoing that I grew up to become a veterinarian, or a rabbit breeder, or at least one of those mild-mannered, animal-enamored ladies who keep rabbits in cages behind their compost heaps. However my interest in these creatures has never been very practical. There's something in their timorousness, in their graceful, streaking run that prevents me from considering them as commodities or pets. William Cowper has assured us that hares make diverting companions, and I've no doubt they do. Yet they don't really appear to need us, not like dogs and, yes, cats do. I can't believe that rabbits or hares prefer our hutches, our litter boxes, our nuzzling, our fond gibberish to their homes and each other the way their canine and feline counterparts do. I like to think of rabbits and hares as existing on the periphery of human concerns, flitting in and out of our lives and, in the rare moments when we happen to catch sight of them, enchanting and delighting us.

Such a concept is admittedly romantic in the extreme. But it is not unique – poets, novelists and artists have been idealizing the "Animal of Venus" for centuries. On the other hand that concept is far from standard. Farmers, harassed by multitudes of lettuce munchers, have always viewed them with a jaundiced or exasperated eye, while hunters generally have been impressed solely by their speed and alertness. Naturalists and philosophers have been taken with their fecundity, their preposterous ears and hopping gait, and storytellers and mythmakers, being less empirically inclined individuals, have concentrated on the multifarious aspects of their characters and the effects (beneficial or hazardous depending on who's telling the tale) of their physical presence.

As this book attempts to illustrate, one's idea of these animals clearly depends upon one's experience and sensibilities. Yet most of the disparate accounts of rabbits and hares contained in the following pages are united, if not in theme, in passion and dogmatism. The rabbit and hare are wretched, they are carefree, they are cunning, humble, hermaphroditic, fearful, lucky, charmed – so pronounce the sages from Aristotle to Robert Burns.

The truth is, the sages are all right, each in his own way, because the rabbit and hare are, inevitably, a mystery – a long-eared, quivering-nosed, carrot-eating mystery – and like any good mystery, they can be appreciated on many levels, but they can never be fully understood.

B. P. *October 1981*.

CHAPTER ONE

Burning the Wind

Poets, novelists, hunters and
naturalists admire the silent,
watchful nature and lightning
speed of the elusive rabbit
and its cousin the hare.

March Hares

"The best way to go," said my muffled-up friend, "is to look in
  its *form* for a Hare, you know;"
So, with gun over shoulder, we sallied out early, the bushes all
  hunched up with snow, you know;
The dawn was still under the eastern horizon, and O but the
  morning was rare, you know;
The elms and the oaks were a-dangle with ice, that swayed in
  the breeze to and fro, you know –
Icicles half a yard long at the least, that tinkled and rang in the
  air, you know;
"A marvellous music," said I to my friend; and he, he never
  said, No, you know.

The snow had been falling for days, there were drifts full
  fifteen feet deep, and so fair, you know,
Aurora herself might have looked to her blushes, and Cupid
  have trimmed up his bow, you know;
And when o'er the rim of the World came the Sun, and with
  eye like a topaz did glare, you know,
We stood for a while as if blinded with Paradise, dumb in that
  wonderful glow, you know;
We coughed, and we shifted our guns, and went on – no more
  than a cough could we dare, you know,
For moment by moment we couldn't tell where we should
  come within sight of the foe, you know.

And, all of a sudden, my friend, he said, "Ssh!" and I looked
  and I listened; and there, you know –
Not half a shot off, with his ears and his scut, crouching close in
  the lily-white snow, you know,
And his eyes like two blazing bright marbles of glass – sat
  staring and glaring a Hare, you know!
The sun it shone brighter, the blue it grew bluer, the heavens
  like an infinite O, you know,
And a breeze out of nowhere rang sweet as a bell rings, and
  stirred in our whiskers and hair, you know.

My friend – then – he – up – with – his – gun – to – his –
  shoulder – and tugged at the trigger: but lo! you know,
In his kindness of heart he'd forgotten to load, for for slaughter
  he didn't much care, you know;
We laughed, oh! laughed we; and, my ghost! if old Watt
  didn't up with his nose and cry, "Ho!" you know;
And stamped with his brothers and sisters to come; and they
  hopped up in scores from their lairs, you know.
They danced, they fandangoed, they scuttered, they sang,
  turned somersaults, leapfrogged, and so, you know
We trudged back to breakfast with nothing to jug, which
  wasn't *exacaly* fair, you know,
  Which *wasn't* exacaly fair.

Walter de la Mare

The Jackass Rabbit

As the sun was going down, we saw the first specimen of an animal known familiarly over two thousand miles of mountain and desert – from Kansas clear to the Pacific Ocean – as the "jackass rabbit." He is well named. He is just like any other rabbit, except that he is from one-third to twice as large, has longer legs in proportion to his size, and has the most preposterous ears that ever were mounted on any creature *but* a jackass. When he is sitting quiet, thinking about his sins, or is absent-minded or unapprehensive of danger, his majestic ears project above him conspicuously; but the breaking of a twig will scare him nearly to death, and then he tilts his ears back gently and starts for home. All you can see, then, for the next minute, is his long gray form stretched out straight and "streaking it" through the low sage-brush, head erect, eyes right, and ears just canted a little to the rear, but showing you where the animal is, all the time, the same as if he carried a jib. Now and then he makes a marvelous spring with his long legs, high over the stunted sage-brush, and scores a leap that would make a horse envious. Presently, he comes down to a long, graceful "lope," and shortly he mysteriously disappears. He has crouched behind a sage-bush, and will sit there and listen and tremble until you get within six feet of him, when he will get under way again. But one must shoot at this creature once, if he wishes to see him throw his heart into his heels, and do the best he knows how. He is frightened clear through, now, and he lays his long ears down on his back, straightens himself out like a yardstick every spring he makes, and scatters miles behind him with an easy indifference that is enchanting.

Our party made this specimen "bump himself," as the conductor said. The Secretary started him with a shot from the Colt; I commenced spitting at him with my weapon; and

all in the same instant the old
"Allen's" whole broadside let go with
a rattling crash, and it is not putting it
too strong to say that the rabbit was
frantic! He dropped his ears, set up
his tail, and left for San Francisco at a
speed which can only be described
as a flash and a vanish! Long after he
was out of sight we could hear him
whiz.

Mark Twain

On Seeing a Wounded Hare Limp by Me, Which a Fellow had Just Shot At

1 INHUMAN man! curse on thy barbarous art,
   And blasted be thy murder-aiming eye:
   May never pity soothe thee with a sigh,
Nor ever pleasure glad thy cruel heart!

2 Go, live, poor wanderer of the wood and field!
   The bitter little that of life remains:
   No more the thickening brakes and verdant plains
To thee shall home, or food, or pastime yield.

3 Seek, mangled wretch! some place of wonted rest,
   No more of rest, but now thy dying bed!
   The sheltering rushes whistling o'er thy head,
The cold earth with thy bloody bosom press'd.

4 Oft as by winding Nith, I, musing, wait
   The sober eve, or hail the cheerful dawn,
   I'll miss thee sporting o'er the dewy lawn,
And curse the ruffian's aim, and mourn thy hapless
   fate.

Robert Burns

Molly Cotton-Tail

At the first creek I stopped on the bridge and rested against the railing. In a few minutes I saw two rabbits hop across the road ahead. Picking up the gun I started after them. A hundred yards from the bridge the road had been cut down into the hill and the banks on each side were fifteen and twenty feet high. At this time of year, when there was nearly always a heavy frost each morning, the bank facing the south was the warmer because the sun shone against it most of the day. I had seen several rabbits sitting in holes in the bank, and I was sure that was where these rabbits were going now.

Sure enough, when I got there a large gray-furred rabbit was sitting on the sunny bank backed into a hole. When I saw the rabbit I raised the shotgun to my shoulder and took good aim. The rabbit blinked her eyes and chewed a piece of grass she had found under a log somewhere. I was then only ten or twelve feet away, but I thought I had better get closer so I should be certain to kill her. I would take the rabbit home and show my aunt. I wanted her to invite me to spend the summer at her house again.

I edged closer and closer to the rabbit until I stood in the drain ditch only three feet from her. She blinked her eyes and chewed on the grass. I hated to kill her because she looked as if she wanted to live and sit on the sunny bank chewing grass always. But my Aunt Nellie thought a boy should be a sportsman and kill everything in sight.

There was nothing else I could do. I would have to shoot the poor rabbit and take her back for my aunt to see.

I took steady aim along the center of the double-barreled shotgun, shut both eyes, and pulled the triggers one after the other. When I opened my eyes the rabbit was still sitting there looking at me. I was so glad after the gun went off that the rabbit was not dead that I dropped the gun and crawled up the bank and caught the rabbit by her long ears. I lifted her in my arms and held her tightly so she could not run away. She was so frightened by the gunshots she was trembling all over like a whipped dog. When I put her in my arms she snuggled her nose against my sweater and stopped quivering while I stroked her fur.

Holding the rabbit tight in my right arm I picked up the shotgun and ran home as fast as I could.

My father was still sitting in the back yard when I got there.

"What's that you've got under your arm?" he asked.

"A rabbit," I told him.

"How did you catch it?"

"I shot at her and missed her. Then I caught her by the ears and brought her home."

"Look here, Johnny," he said to me. "You didn't shoot at that rabbit while it was sitting down, did you?"

"I guess I did," I admitted; adding hastily, "but I didn't hit her, anyway."

"Well, it's a good thing you didn't hit it. A good sportsman never shoots at a rabbit while it is sitting down. A good sportsman never shoots at a bird until it flies. A real sportsman always gives the game he is after a chance for its life."

"But Aunt Nellie said I had to kill something and she didn't say not to kill things standing still."

"You stop paying any attention to your Aunt Nellie. She doesn't know what she's talking about anyway."

I let my father hold the rabbit while I fixed a box to keep her in. When I was ready I put her in it and shut her up tight.

"What are you going to do with the rabbit?" he asked me.

"Keep her."

"I wouldn't put it in a box," he said with a queer look on his face. "If it wants to stay it won't run off. And if it doesn't want to stay it will worry itself to death in that box all the time. Turn it loose and let's see what it will do."

I was afraid to turn my rabbit loose

because I did not want her to run away. But my father knew a lot more about rabbits than I did. Just then Aunt Nellie and my mother came out on the back porch.

"What have you got there in the box?" Aunt Nellie asked me.

"A rabbit," I said.

"Where did you get it?"

"I shot at her with the gun but I didn't hit her and she didn't run away so I brought her home."

My aunt turned to my mother in disgust.

"There you are, Bess! What did I tell you?"

I did not hear what my mother said. But my father got up and went down to the barn. Aunt Nellie went into the house and slammed shut the door behind her. My mother stood looking at me for several minutes as if I had done the right thing after all.

Taking the rabbit out of the box I went down to the barn where my father was. He was sitting against the barn side shelling an ear of corn for half a dozen chickens around him. I sat down beside him and turned the rabbit loose. The rabbit hopped around and around and then sat down and looked at us.

"Why don't you name it Molly Cotton-Tail?" my father suggested, throwing a handful of shelled corn to the chickens.

"What does that mean?" I asked.

"There are two kinds of rabbits around here: jack rabbits and molly cotton-tails. That one has a cotton-tail — see the ball of white fur on its tail that looks like a boll of cotton?"

The rabbit hopped around and around again and sat down on her cotton-tail. The chickens were not afraid of her. They went right up to where she sat and scratched for corn just as if she had been a chicken too.

"Why don't you go into the garden and get a head of lettuce for it? Get a good tender one out of the hot-bed. All rabbits like lettuce," he said.

I got the lettuce and gave it to my rabbit. She hopped up to where we

sat against the barn side, asking for more. I gave her all I had and she ate out of my hand.

"If you had killed that rabbit with the gun you would be sorry now," my father said. Anybody could see that he was beginning to like my rabbit a lot.

She hopped around and around in front of us, playing with the chickens. The chickens liked her, too.

"I'd lots rather have her living than dead," I said, suddenly realizing how much I liked her myself.

Molly hopped up between us and nibbled at my father's hand. He reached to stroke her fur with his hand but she hopped away.

"Whoa there, sooky," he soothed, reaching for our rabbit.

Erskine Caldwell

Ole Molly Hare

"**O**le Molly Hare, what you doin' there?"
"Runnin' through the cotton patch hard as I can tear."

"Bru'r Rabbit, Bru'r Rabbit, what makes your ears so long?"
"Cause, by God, they're put on wrong."

"Bru'r Rabbit, Bru'r Rabbit, what makes you look so shy?"
"Cause, my Lord, I don't want to die."

"Bru'r Rabbit, Bru'r Rabbit, what makes you look so thin?"
"Cause, by God, I'm burning the wind."

"Bru'r Rabbit, Bru'r Rabbit, what makes your tail so white?"
"Cause, by God, I'm going out of sight."

American Folk Song

All Things that Love the Sun

All things that love the sun are out of doors;
The sky rejoices in the morning's birth;
The grass is bright with rain-drops; – on the moors
The hare is running races in her mirth;
And with her feet she from the plashy earth
Raises a mist, that glittering in the sun,
Runs with her all the way, wherever she doth run.

William Wordsworth from Resolution and
Independence

Beatrix Potter's Pets

Perhaps of all her pets, the ones that meant most to her were the rabbits. She had two Belgian rabbits (two bucks in succession), the first called Benjamin Bunny (commonly known as "Bounce"), the second, Peter. When cold they used to tuck their forepaws backwards under the fur and lie upon them. "Both were fond of the fire, and one used to lie inside the fender; I have even seen him asleep under the grate on the hot ashes when the fire had gone out," she wrote.

From The Art of Beatrix Potter

Jack Rabbit

The borrowed light went through the dark
where a beast with petals on his head
sent the light back from one wild eye
and turned his haunches into stone.
My hill is high; the ditch pretends
to shelter wanderers like these,
but there's a curve where power counts
against fluff scrambling onto roads
we built to carry our own lives
between black trees and staring weed.
He huddled into fear and stayed.
Below, a town of ignorant frogs
squatting in some unrented pond
stroked like one green and noisy heart.

One of us would have to wait,
or gamble for the right-of-way.
I had seen the losers stretched
along the highway's stinging belt,
small carpets laid out suddenly
beneath an unequivocal tire.

He kept within his stapled bones
and still his eye looked out and gleamed.
My brakes were never meant to hold
On such a slant for such as he
caught in a habit of response
too old to change. And yet I stopped.
And yet I spoke
until he turned and easily took
his tail and ears up the same road.
My car, a thundering shepherd, coaxed
him over the hill, and I went on.

Adrien Stoutenberg

Light Foot

The hares (*Lepus Americanus*) were very familiar. One had her form under my house all winter, separated from me only by the flooring, and she startled me each morning by her hasty departure when I began to stir, – thump, thump, thump, striking her head against the floor timbers in her hurry. They used to come round my door at dusk to nibble the potato parings which I had thrown out, and were so nearly the color of the ground that they could hardly be distinguished when still. Sometimes in the twilight I alternately lost and recovered sight of one sitting motionless under my window. When I opened my door in the evening, off they would go with a squeak and a bounce. Near at hand they only excited my pity. One evening one sat by my door two paces from me, at first trembling with fear, yet unwilling to move; a poor wee thing, lean and bony, with ragged ears and sharp nose, scant tail and slender paws. It looked as if Nature no longer contained the breed of nobler bloods, but stood on her last toes. Its large eyes appeared young and unhealthy, almost dropsical. I took a step, and lo, away it scud with an elastic spring over the snow crust, straightening its body and its limbs into graceful length, and soon put the forest between me and itself, – the wild free venison, asserting its vigor and the dignity of Nature. Not without reason was, its slenderness. Such then was its nature. (*Lepus*, *levipes*, lightfoot some think.)

Henry David Thoreau from Walden

The White Rabbit

He is white as Helvellyn when winter is well in;
  His whiskers are mobile and tender.
If it weren't for the greed that compels him to feed
  Without ceasing, his form would be slender.

With elegant hops he crushes or crops
  All the flowers that bloom in the garden;
Yet such is the grace that suffuses his face,
  He wins, without asking, our pardon.

The Sun, who rides heaven from Dover to Devon
  Inspecting furred folk and their habits,
Breaks out into poesy: "What summer snow is he
  Made of, this pearl among rabbits?"

And at night on the lawn as he waits for the dawn,
  Rapt in dreams of a rabbit's perfection,
The Moon in her stride sweeps the cloudlets aside
  To rejoice in his silver reflection.

E. V. Rieu

Song of the Rabbits Outside a Tavern

We who play under the pines,
We who dance in the snow
That shines blue in the light of the moon
Sometimes halt as we go,
Stand with our ears erect,
Our noses testing the air
To gaze at the golden world
Behind the windows there.

Suns they have in a cave,
And stars each on a tall white stem,
And the thought of fox or of owl
Seems never to trouble them.
They laugh and eat and are warm,
Their food is ready at hand,
While hungry out in the cold
We little rabbits stand.

But they never dance as we dance,
They have not the speed nor the grace,
We scorn both the cat and the dog
Who lie by their fireplace,
We scorn them, licking their paws
Their eyes on an upraised spoon –
We who dance hungry and wild
Under a winter's moon!

Elizabeth Coatsworth

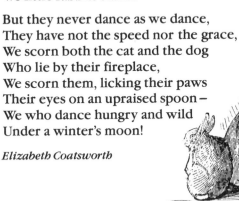

A Rabbit as King of the Ghosts

The difficulty to think at the end of the day,
When the shapeless shadow covers the sun
And nothing is left except light on your fur –

There was the cat slopping its milk all day,
Fat cat, red tongue, green mind, white milk
And August the most peaceful month.

To be, in the grass, in the peacefullest time,
Without that monument of cat,
The cat forgotten in the moon;

And to feel that the light is a rabbit-light,
In which everything is meant for you
And nothing need be explained;

Then there is nothing to think of. It comes of itself;
And east rushes west and west rushes down,
No matter. The grass is full

And full of yourself. The trees around are for you,
The whole of the wideness of night is for you,
A self that touches all edges,

You become a self that fills the four corners of night.
The red cat hides away in the fur-light
And there you are humped high, humped up,

You are humped higher and higher, black as stone –
You sit with your head like a carving in space
And the little green cat is a bug in the grass.

Wallace Stevens

Some Fearful Hare

SO have I seen some fearful hare maintain
A course, till tir'd before the dog she lay;
Who, stretch'd behind her, pants upon the plain,
Past pow'r to kill, as she to get away:

With his loll'd tongue he faintly licks his prey;
His warm breath blows her flix up as she lies;
She, trembling, creeps upon the ground away,
And looks back to him with beseeching eyes.

John Dryden from Annus Mirabilis

CHAPTER TWO

There Once Was a Rabbit

By all accounts rabbits and hares are
exceedingly complex animals.
At one and the same time they're
lazy, industrious, clever, gullible,
meek and vexatious – ideal subjects
of legends and cautionary tales.

The Moon and his Younger Sister

The moon was formerly a handsome, white-faced Indian. The stars were his friends. The hare was his younger sister. Once upon a time he called the Pleiades and all the other stars to his house, but only the star cluster came. They are named the Pleiades. Yet the house was crowded, so that some of them had no place to sit. After the guests had all arrived, the moon sent his younger sister to fetch some water. She took her water-buckets and left. Ere long she returned carrying a bucket in each hand. When she had entered, she said to her brother, "There is no place for me to sit." Her elder brother replied, "Sit here on my face, for there is no room elsewhere." His sister jumped on to his face. If the moon had not joked in this manner, he would now be much brighter, for his sister is darkening his brightness. The woman may still be seen sitting on the moon's face, holding her water-buckets; and because the Pleiades gathered in his house, they form a cluster up to this day, and travel the way they follow now. They are the moon's closest friends.

A Thompson River Indian Legend

How Mr. Rabbit Lost his Fine Bushy Tail

"One time," said Uncle Remus, sighing heavily and settling himself back in his seat with an air of melancholy resignation – "one time Brer Rabbit wuz gwine 'long down de road shakin' his big bushy tail, en feelin' des ez scrumpshus ez a bee-martin wid a fresh bug." Here the old man paused and glanced at the little boy, but it was evident that the youngster had become so accustomed to the marvelous developments of Uncle Remus's stories, that the extraordinary statement made no unusual impression upon him. Therefore the old man began again, and this time in a louder and more insinuating tone:

"One time ole man Rabbit, he was gwine 'long down de road shakin' his long, bushy tail, en feelin' mighty biggity."

This was effective.

"Great goodness, Uncle Remus!" exclaimed the boy in open-eyed wonder, "everybody knows that rabbits haven't got long, bushy tails."

The old man shifted his position in his chair and allowed his venerable head to drop forward until his whole appearance was suggestive of the deepest dejection; and this was intensified by a groan that seemed to be the result of great mental agony. Finally he spoke, but not as addressing himself to the little boy.

"I notices dat dem fokes w'at makes a great 'miration 'bout w'at dey knows is des de fokes w'ich you can't put no 'pennunce in w'en de 'cashun come up. Yer one un um now, en he done come en excuse me er 'lowin' dat rabbits is got long, bushy tails, w'ich goodness know ef

I'd a dremp it, I'd whirl in en on
dremp it."

"Well, but Uncle Remus, you said
rabbits had long bushy tails," replied
the little boy. "Now you know you
did."

"Ef I ain't fergit it off'n my mine, I
say dat ole Brer Rabbit wuz gwine
down de big road shakin' his long,
bushy tail. Dat w'at I say, en dat I
stan's by."

The little boy looked puzzled, but
he didn't say anything. After a while
the old man continued:

"Now, den, ef dat's 'greed ter, I'm
gwine on, en ef tain't 'greed ter, den
I'm gwineter pick up my cane en
look atter my own intrust. I got wuk
lyin' 'roun' yer dat's des natally gittin'
moldy."

The little boy still remained quiet,
and Uncle Remus proceeded:

"One day Brer Rabbit wuz gwine
down de road shakin' his long, bushy
tail, w'en who should he strike up
wid but ole Brer Fox gwine amblin'
long wid a big string er fish! W'en

dey pass de time er day wid wunner nudder, Brer Rabbit, he open up de confab, he did, en he ax Brer Fox whar he git dat nice string er fish, en Brer Fox, he up'n 'spon' dat he katch um, en Brer Rabbit, he say whar'bouts, en Brer Fox, he say down at de baptizin' creek, en Brer Rabbit he ax how, kaze in dem days dey wuz monstus fon' er minners, en Brer Fox, he sot down on a log, he did, en he up'n tell Brer Rabbit dat all he gotter do fer ter git er big mess er minners is ter go ter de creek atter sun down, en drap his tail in de water en set dar twel day-light, en den draw up a whole armful er fishes, en dem w'at he don't want, he kin fling back. Right dar's whar Brer Rabbit drap his watermillion, kaze he tuck'n sot out dat night en went a fishin'. De wedder wuz sorter cole, en Brer Rabbit, he got 'im a bottle er dram en put out fer de creek, en w'en he git dar he pick out a good place, en he sorter squot down, he did, en let his tail hang in de water. He sot dar, en

he sot dar, en he drunk his dram, en he think he gwineter freeze, but bimeby day come, en dar he wuz. He make a pull, en he feel like he comin' in two, en he fetch nudder jerk, en lo en beholes, whar wuz his tail?"

There was a long pause.

"Did it come off, Uncle Remus?" asked the little boy, presently.

"She did dat!" replied the old man with unction. "She did dat, and dat w'at make all deze yer bob-tail rabbits w'at you see hoppin' en skaddlin' thoo de woods."

"Are they all that way just because the old Rabbit lost his tail in the creek?" asked the little boy.

"Dat's it, honey," replied the old man. "Dat's w'at dey tells me. Look like dey er bleedzd ter take atter der pa."

Joel Chandler Harris from Uncle Remus, his Songs and his Sayings

Most Humble Hare

Once upon a time there was a forest glade where holy men came to meditate, a beautiful, natural garden filled with fruits and flowers, carpeted with tender grass and refreshed by the waters of a sparkling stream, blue as lapis-lazuli. Now in this little paradise there lived a hare, a creature whose many virtues gave him ascendancy over all the other animals. By precept and example he taught his companions to perform their religious duties in a manner approved by the pious, until "their renown reached even the world of the Devas."

One evening the Buddha came to his garden. Certain of his disciples accompanied the Holy One, sitting reverently at his feet and listening while he preached the Law. All night long he discoursed and until the next day at high noon, when the sun darts his sharpest beam; when the horizon, enclosed in a net of trembling rays of light and veiled with radiant heat, does not suffer itself to be looked upon, when the cicadae shriek their loudest; when no living creature leaves the shelter of the shade, and the vigor of travelers is exhausted by heat and fatigue.

In that time of the day, the Buddha chose to assume the figure of a Brahman, crying out like one who has lost his road and is consumed with weariness and sorrow:

"Alone and astray, having lost my companions, I am a-hunger and a-thirst! Help me, ye pious!"

All the little forest-dwellers heard the cry of distress, and one by one they hastened to the Holy Man, begging him wander no further but remain with them and accept their hospitality. And each, according to his means, brought food for him. The otter brought seven fishes, saying: "Accept these, and remain with us." The jackal brought his kill, saying:

"Honor us with thy presence and grant us Thy instruction." When it came to the turn of the hare, he approached empty-handed and said humbly:

"Master, I who have grown up in the forest, nourished by the grass and herbs, have nothing to offer thee but my own body. Grant us the boon of resting Thy Holiness in this place, and vouchsafe to me the favor of feeding thee with my own flesh, since I have nothing else to give thee."

Even as he spoke, the hare perceived a heap of magic charcoal burning without smoke nearby. He was about to leap into the flames when he paused and began gently picking out the little creatures lodging in his fur. "My body I may sacrifice to the Holy One," he murmured, "but your lives I have no right to take." He placed the tiny insects safely on the ground, and then with the utmost gladness, like one desirous of wealth on beholding a treasure, threw himself into that blazing fire.

Resuming his own form, the Buddha praised the loftiness of the sacrifice:

"He who forgets self, be he the humblest of earthly creatures, will reach the Ocean of Eternal Peace. Let all men learn from this example and be persuaded to deeds of compassion and mercy."

Moreover, to reward the hare Buddha commanded that his image should adorn the disc of the moon, a shining example for all time. As for the other animals of the forest, they were translated to the world of the Devas, thanks to their holy friend. Ever since these happenings in the forest, the moon has been known to the Buddhist world as the "Hare-marked."

A Birth Story of Buddha

The Hare and the Hound

A hound having started a hare from his form, after a long run, gave up the chase. A goat-herd, seeing him stop, mocked him, saying, "The little one is the best runner of the two." The hound replied, "You do not see the differences between us: I was only running for a dinner, but he, for his life."

Aesop

The Tortoise and the Hare

There was once a wise young tortoise who read in an ancient book about a tortoise who had beaten a hare in a race. He read all the other books he could find but in none of them was there any record of a hare who had beaten a tortoise. The wise young tortoise came to the natural conclusion that he could outrun a hare, so he set forth in search of one. In his wanderings he met many animals who were willing to race him: weasels, stoats, dachshunds, badger-boars, short-tailed field mice and ground squirrels. But when the tortoise asked if they could outrun a hare, they all said no, they couldn't (with the exception of a dachshund named Freddy, and nobody paid any attention to him). "Well, I can," said the tortoise, "so there's no use wasting my time on you." And he continued his search.

After many days, the tortoise finally encountered a hare and challenged him to a race. "What are you going to use for legs?" asked the hare. "Never mind that," said the tortoise. "Read this." He showed the hare the story in the ancient book, complete with moral about the swift not always being so terribly fast. 'Tosh," said the hare. "You couldn't go fifty feet in an hour and a half, whereas I can go fifty feet in one and a fifth seconds." "Posh," said the tortoise. "You probably won't even finish second." "We'll see about that," said the hare. So they marked off a course fifty feet long. All the other animals gathered around. A bullfrog set them on their marks, a gun dog fired a pistol, and they were off.

When the hare crossed the finish line, the tortoise had gone approximately eight and three-quarter inches.

Moral: A new broom may sweep clean, but never trust an old saw.

James Thurber

The Hare and the Tortoise

A hare one day ridiculed the short feet and slow pace of the tortoise. The latter, laughing, said: "Though you be swift as the wind, I will beat you in a race." The hare, deeming her assertion to be simply impossible, assented to the proposal; and they agreed that the fox should choose the course and fix the goal. On the day appointed for the race they started together. The tortoise never for a moment stopped, but went on with a slow but steady pace straight to the end of the course. The hare, trusting to his native swiftness, cared little about the race, and laying down by the wayside, fell fast asleep. At last waking up, and moving as fast as he could, he saw the tortoise had reached the goal and was comfortably dozing after her fatigue.

Aesop

The Hare and the Frogs

In his form a hare would meditate;
For what can a hare do in his form but dream?
Devoured by apprehension, his fear was so great:
The creature was sad – every nerve shivering it would seem.
  "When persons are born timorous,"
  He said, "it make them dolorous.
Every morsel tastes queer which they attempt to eat;
Joy is not joy because of quivers everywhere.
I don't exaggerate; not even sleep is sweet.
Since focused on thin air, my two eyes stare and stare.
Curb your fears, moralists say, and all will be well.
  Fear cure itself? But when has that been possible?
  Perhaps these strong fears stabbing me,
  Stab human beings equally."
  So he mused, and quivered in his fright
  While he maintained a sharp lookout –
  Shivering and glancing about:
Some shadow or sound shot his fever to a height.
  The melancholy animal,
  Musing on his despair,
Took a slight rustle as a sign that the blow must fall
  And darted away to his lair,
Skirting a pond by which a footpath chanced to run.
Frogs at once sprang from wherever they hid.
Frogs sprang into the grottoes they had in the mud.

"Ah," he said, "I'm not the only one
   In whom fear is stirred, since by chance
I find I've caused it, creating panic as others have done!
   I too have broken a lance!
How so! I induce timidity? I stun?
   A cannonading thunderer?
There is, I see, no coward anywhere
   So craven he can't find a greater one."

La Fontaine

Down the Rabbit-Hole

Alice was beginning to get very tired of sitting by her sister on the bank, and of having nothing to do: once or twice she had peeped into the book her sister was reading, but it had no pictures or conversations in it, "and what is the use of a book," thought Alice, "without pictures or conversations?"

So she was considering in her own mind (as well as she could, for the hot day made her feel very sleepy and stupid) whether the pleasure of making a daisy-chain would be worth the trouble of getting up and picking the daisies, when suddenly a White Rabbit with pink eyes ran close by her.

There was nothing so very remarkable in that; nor did Alice think it so very much out of the way to hear the Rabbit say to itself, "Oh dear! Oh dear! I shall be too late!" (when she thought it over afterwards, it occurred to her that she ought to have wondered at this, but at the time it all seemed quite natural); but

when the Rabbit actually took a watch out of its waistcoat-pocket, and looked at it, and then hurried on, Alice started to her feet, for it flashed across her mind that she had never before seen a rabbit with either a waistcoat-pocket or a watch to take out of it, and, burning with curiosity, she ran across the field after it, and was just in time to see it pop down a large rabbit-hole under the hedge.

In another moment down went Alice after it, never once considering how in the world she was to get out again.

Lewis Carroll from Alice in Wonderland

A Rabbit Parable

In Wildwood, a socially eminent Rabbit,
Of dignity, substance and girth,
Had chosen a suitable hole to inhabit –
An excellent burrow of earth.

When up came a Woodchuck, a genuine Groundhog,
Who wanted the place for his lair;
The Rabbit, impressed by a seventeen-pound Hog,
Abruptly departed from there.

But shortly thereafter a virtuous Badger
Slid down from a neighboring shelf;
The Woodchuck he slew as a robber and cadger,
Bequeathing the hole to himself.

A Fox who believed in the law of requital
Appeared through the bordering fern;
He questioned the Badger's manorial title,
Demanding the burrow in turn.

A battle ensued in a terrible smother,
Affrighting the hardiest soul;
The Fox and the Badger abolished each other,
The Rabbit returned to his hole.

So here is appended the mildest of morals,
Accept it for what it is worth:
"When all of the Haughty are killed in their quarrels
The Meek shall inherit the earth."

Arthur Guiterman

Rabbit Has a Busy Day

It was going to be one of Rabbit's busy days. As soon as he woke up he felt important, as if everything depended upon him. It was just the day for Organizing Something, or for Writing a Notice Signed Rabbit, or for Seeing What Everybody Else Thought About It. It was a perfect morning for hurrying round to Pooh, and saying, "Very well, then, I'll tell Piglet," and then going to Piglet, and saying, "Pooh thinks – but perhaps I'd better see Owl first." It was a Captainish sort of day, when everybody said "Yes, Rabbit" and "No, Rabbit," and waited until he had told them.

He came out of his house and sniffed the warm spring morning as he wondered what he would do. Kanga's house was nearest, and at Kanga's house was Roo, who said "Yes, Rabbit" and "No, Rabbit" almost better than anybody else in the Forest; but there was another animal there nowadays, the strange and

Bouncy Tigger; and he was the sort of Tigger who was always in front when you were showing him the way anywhere, and was generally out of sight when at last you came to the place and said proudly "Here we are!"

"No, not Kanga's," said Rabbit thoughtfully to himself, as he curled his whiskers in the sun; and, to make quite sure that he wasn't going there, he turned to the left and trotted off in the other direction, which was the way to Christopher Robin's house.

"After all," said Rabbit to himself, "Christopher Robin depends on Me. He's fond of Pooh and Piglet and Eeyore, and so am I, but they haven't any Brain. Not to notice. And he respects Owl, because you can't help respecting anybody who can spell TUESDAY, even if he doesn't spell it right; but spelling isn't everything. There are days when spelling Tuesday simply doesn't count. And Kanga is too busy looking after Roo, and Roo is too young and Tigger is too bouncy to be any help, so there's really nobody but Me, when you come to look at it. I'll go and see if there's anything he wants doing, and then I'll do it for him. It's just the day for doing things."

He trotted along happily, and by-and-by he crossed the stream and came to the place where his friends-and-relations lived. There seemed to be even more of them about than usual this morning, and having nodded to a hedgehog or two, with whom he was too busy to shake hands, and having said, "Good morning, good morning," importantly to some of the others, and "Ah, there

you are," kindly, to the smaller ones, he waved a paw at them over his shoulder, and was gone; leaving such an air of excitement and I-don't-know-what behind him, that several members of the Beetle family, including Henry Rush, made their way at once to the Hundred Acre Wood and began climbing trees, in the hope of getting to the top before it happened, whatever it was, so that they might see it properly.

Rabbit hurried on by the edge of the Hundred Acre Wood, feeling

more important every minute, and soon he came to the tree where Christopher Robin lived. He knocked on the door, and he called out once or twice, and then he walked back a little way and put his paw up to keep the sun out, and called to the top of the tree, and then he turned all round and shouted "Hallo!" and "I say!" "It's Rabbit!" – but nothing happened. Then he stopped and listened, and everything stopped and listened with him, and the Forest was very lone and still and peaceful in the sunshine, until suddenly a hundred miles above him a lark began to sing.

"Bother!" said Rabbit. "He's gone out."

He went back to the green front door, just to make sure, and he was turning away, feeling that his morning had got all spoilt, when he saw a piece of paper on the ground. And there was a pin in it, as if it had fallen off the door.

"Ha!" said Rabbit, feeling quite happy again. "Another notice!"

This is what it said:

GON OUT
BACKSON
BISY
BACKSON
C.R.

"Ha!" said Rabbit again. "I must tell the others." And he hurried off importantly.

The nearest house was Owl's, and to Owl's House in the Hundred Acre Wood he made his way. He came to Owl's door, and he knocked and he rang, and he rang and he knocked, and at last Owl's head came out and said "Go away, I'm thinking – oh, it's you?" which was how he always began.

"Owl," said Rabbit shortly, "you and I have brains. The others have fluff. If there is any thinking to be done in this Forest – and when I say thinking I mean *thinking* – you and I must do it."

A. A. Milne from The House at Pooh Corner

Peter Rabbit

1. **P**eter Rabbit's
   Mother sighed,
   "Son, you'd better
   Stay inside."

   Peter Rabbit's
   Father said,
   "Don't you dare
   Get out of bed!

   "For if you do
   You'll sneak away
   And like a shot
   You'll go and play

"In Farmer J.
MacGregor's garden –
Planning, without
A beg-your-pardon,

"To bolt his luscious
Turnips down
While we are shopping
In the town."

Peter yawned
At this to-do.
"So what?' he asked.
"You eat them too."

"It's not at all
The same," they said,
From either side
Of his messy bed,

"For since you will not
Use your spoon,
You'll turn into
A Spotted Goon!"

2. "Shut up, dear parents,"
   Peter cried,
   "You know I'd never
   Sneak outside

   "And wolf those luscious
   Turnips down,
   While you are shopping
   In the town!"

   Then Peter hummed
   A loving hum,
   And watched his tired old
   Dad and mum

Teetering out
And tottering down
The steep steep hill
To the shops in town.

3. Then up he sprang
And off he sped
With visions of turnips
Alive in his head;

And up he rose
And off he ran
To where the turnip
Patch began.

He pulled up one.
He pulled up two.
He stuffed them in
And gave a chew.

And down they went
Kerplunk, because –
He crammed them in
With just his paws!

4. When woe betide us!
Lack-a-day!
Good gosh, gadzooks and
Wellaway!

Quick, thick and fast
In inky blots
His fur broke out
With horrid spots.

He raced inside
To find a mirror;
The awful change
Grew clear and clearer:

Without a doubt
He was a Goon –
Because he would not
Use a spoon!

5. Is this the end
Of Peter's tale?
A Goon-like life
In a spotted jail?

No, no! Again
I say it – No!
Great heavens! let it
Not be so!

For thinking of
His dreadful doom
He cried, "I Should Have
Used a Spoon!"

And pondering
His piteous plight
He roared, "My Dad
And Mum Were Right!"

At once his face
Began to shine.
He lit up like
A neon sign

Till someone put him
On TV
And parents forced
Their kids to see

The Shiny Spotted
Goody-Goon,
Who *Never* Ate
Without a Spoon.

Well, that's the story.
Here's the moral:
"Hare today
And Goon tomorrow."

Dennis Lee

CHAPTER THREE

Prince With a Thousand Enemies

Stories, poems and essays maligning the rabbit are as numerous as they are impassioned. Perhaps the detractors envy its fertility or are incensed by its vegetable-patch larceny. More likely, though, they find its fleeting presence somewhat too disturbing to dismiss.

The Rabbit who Caused all the Trouble

Within the memory of the youngest child there was a family of rabbits who lived near a pack of wolves. The wolves announced that they did not like the way the rabbits were living. (The wolves were crazy about the way they themselves were living, because it was the only way to live.) One night several wolves were killed in an earthquake and this was blamed on the rabbits, for it is well known that rabbits pound on the ground with their hind legs and cause earthquakes. On another night one of the wolves was killed by a bolt of lightning and this was also blamed on the rabbits, for it is well known that lettuce-eaters cause lightning. The wolves threatened to civilize the rabbits if they didn't behave, and the rabbits decided to run away to a desert island. But the other animals, who lived at a great distance, shamed them, saying, "You must stay where you are and be brave. This is no world for escapists. If the wolves attack you, we will come to your aid, in all probability." So the rabbits continued to live near the wolves and one day there was a terrible flood which drowned a great many wolves. This was blamed on the rabbits, for it is well known that carrot-nibblers with long ears cause floods. The wolves descended on the rabbits, for their own good, and imprisoned them in a dark cave, for their own protection.

When nothing was heard about the rabbits for some weeks, the other animals demanded to know what had happened to them. The wolves replied that the rabbits had been eaten, and since they had been eaten the affair was a purely internal matter. But the other animals warned that they might possibly unite against the wolves unless some reason was given for the destruction of the rabbits.

So the wolves gave them one. "They were trying to escape," said the wolves, "and, as you know, this is no world for escapists."

Moral: Run, don't walk, to the nearest desert island.

James Thurber

ALL the world will be your enemy,
Prince with a Thousand Enemies,
and whenever they catch you, they
will kill you. But first they must
catch you, digger, listener, runner,
prince with the swift warning. Be
cunning and full of tricks and your
people shall never be destroyed.

Richard Adams

Even Hares Trample on Conquered Lions

You are the hare of whom the
proverb goes,
Whose valor plucks dead lions by the
beard.

William Shakespeare, King John

How the Rabbit Stole the Otter's Coat

The animals were always arguing about their good looks. Some made a good appearance indeed in their brown coats. Others looked well in their black or gray outfits. Those who had rings on their tails thought themselves, oh, so very much better looking than the ones who had no tails at all. So finally they held a meeting to decide who had the most beautiful coat.

The animals had heard that the otter had the prettiest coat of all. But he lived away up the creek and hardly ever visited the other animals. However, they were sure that he would appear if he heard about the contest for animal beauty laurels.

Now the selfish rabbit decided to keep the otter from getting the prize, because he wanted to win first place himself. And, without telling a soul, he went to the otter's home.

"I've been sent to bring you to the council," he told the otter. "The ani-mals thought you might not know the road." The otter thanked him for his kindness and the two of them set out together for the council ground.

One day on the trip the rabbit made a paddle. "What is that for?" inquired the otter.

"Oh," said the rabbit, "when I sleep with a paddle under my head I have good dreams." By and by the rabbit cleared a path down to the river.

"Why do you do this?" asked the otter.

"This is called 'The place Where It Rains Fire'," replied the rabbit. "Often it rains fire here. Suppose you sleep and I'll watch. If the fire comes I'll call you so that you can jump into the river. Be sure to hang your coat on a tree so it won't be burned."

So the otter hung up his pretty coat of soft, dark-brown fur and went to sleep. This was the rabbit's chance to trick otter. He put hot coals on the paddle and tossed them up in the air. "Oh! oh! It's raining fire!" he cried. The poor frightened otter then ran and jumped into the river. And he has lived in the water ever since.

Then the tricky rabbit put on otter's coat and sallied forth to the council. When the animals saw him coming they shouted: "Here comes otter!" They wondered why the otter kept his head down, with one paw over his face. But suddenly the bear jerked the paw away. And there sat rabbit. Up he hopped and was scampering away when the bear struck at him. Although rabbit got away, the bear had pulled his tail off. So the rabbit has no tail.

A Cherokee Indian Legend

Bismarck, the Mysterious Demoniacal Rabbit

Gudrun and Winifred went through the house to the back, where were the stables and the out-buildings. Everywhere was still and deserted. Mr. Crich had gone out for a short drive, the stable-man had just led round Gerald's horse. The two girls went to the hutch that stood in a corner, and looked at the great black-and-white rabbit.

"Isn't he beautiful! Oh, do look at him listening! Doesn't he look silly!" she laughed quickly, then added: "Oh, do let's do him listening, do let us, he listens with so much of himself; – don't you, darling Bismarck?"

"Can we take him out?" said Gudrun.

"He's very strong. He really is extremely strong." She looked at Gudrun, her head on one side, in odd calculating mistrust.

"But we'll try shall we?"

"Yes, if you like. But he's a fearful kicker!"

They took the key to unlock the door. The rabbit exploded in a wild rush round the hutch.

"He scratches most awfully sometimes," cried Winifred in excitement. "Oh, do look at him, isn't he wonderful!" The rabbit tore round the hutch in a flurry. "Bismarck!" cried the child, in rousing excitement. "How dreadful you are! You are beastly." Winifred looked up at Gudrun with some misgiving in her wild excitement. Gudrun smiled sardonically with her mouth. Winifred made a strange crooning noise of unaccountable excitement. "Now he's still!" she cried, seeing the rabbit settled down in a far corner of the hutch. "Shall we take him now?" she whispered excitedly, mysteriously, looking up at Gudrun and edging very close. "Shall we get him now? –" she chuckled wickedly to herself.

They unlocked the door of the hutch. Gudrun thrust in her arm and seized the great, lusty rabbit as it crouched still, she grasped its long ears. It set its four feet flat, and thrust back. There was a long scraping sound as it was hauled forward, and in another instant it was in mid-air, lunging wildly, its body flying like a spring coiled and released, as it lashed out, suspended from the ears. Gudrun held the black-and-white tempest at arms' length, averting her face. But the rabbit was magically strong, it was all she could do to keep her grasp. She almost lost her presence of mind.

"Bismarck, Bismarck, you are behaving terribly," said Winifred in a rather frightened voice. "Oh, do put him down, he's beastly."

Gudrun stood for a moment astounded by the thunderstorm that had sprung into being in her grip. Then her colour came up, a heavy rage came over her like a cloud. She stood shaken as a house in a storm, and utterly overcome. Her heart was arrested with fury at the mindlessness and the bestial stupidity of this struggle, her wrists were badly scored by the claws of the beast, a heavy cruelty welled up in her.

Gerald came round as she was trying to capture the flying rabbit under her arm. He saw, with subtle recognition, her sullen passion of cruelty.

"You should let one of the men do that for you," he said hurrying up.

"Oh, he's so horrid!" cried Winifred, almost frantic.

He held out his nervous, sinewy hand and took the rabbit by the ears from Gudrun.

"It's most fearfully strong," she cried in a high voice, like the crying of a seagull, strange and vindictive.

The rabbit made itself into a ball in the air and lashed out, flinging itself into a bow. It really seemed demoniacal. Gudrun saw Gerald's body tighten, saw a sharp blindness come into his eyes.

"I know these beggars of old," he said.

The long, demon-like beast lashed out again, spread on the air as if it were flying, looking something like a dragon, then closing up again, inconceivably powerful and explosive. The man's body, strung to its efforts, vibrated strongly. Then a sudden sharp, white-edged wrath came up in him. Swift as lightning he drew back and brought his free hand down like a hawk on the neck of the rabbit. Simultaneously, there came the unearthly abhorrent scream of a rabbit in the fear of death. It made one immense writhe, tore his wrists and his sleeves in a final convulsion, all its belly flashed white in a whirlwind of paws, and then he had slung it round and had it under his arm fast. It cowered and skulked. His face was gleaming with a smile.

"You wouldn't think there was all that force in a rabbit," he said, looking at Gudrun. And he saw her eyes black as night in her pallid face, she looked almost unearthly. The scream of the rabbit, after the violent tussle, seemed to have torn the veil of her consciousness. He looked at her and the whitish, electric gleam in his face intensified.

"I don't really like him," Winifred was crooning. "I don't care for him as I do for Loozie. He's hateful really."

A smile twisted Gudrun's face as she recovered. She knew she was revealed.

"Don't they make the most fearful noise when they scream?" she cried, the high note in her voice like a seagull's cry.

"Abominable," he said.

"He shouldn't be so silly when he has to be taken out," Winifred was saying, putting out her hand and touching the rabbit tentatively, as it skulked under his arm, motionless as if it were dead.

"He's not dead, is he, Gerald?" she asked.

"No, he ought to be," he said.

"Yes, he ought!" cried the child, with a sudden flush of amusement. And she touched the rabbit with more confidence. "His heart is beating so fast. Isn't he funny? He really is."

"Where do you want him?" asked Gerald.

"In the little green court," she said.

Gudrun looked at Gerald with strange, darkened eyes, strained with underworld knowledge, almost supplicating, like those of a creature which is at his mercy, yet which is his ultimate victor. He did not know what to say to her. He felt the mutual hellish recognition. And he felt he ought to say something to cover it. He had the power of lightning in his nerves, she seemed like a soft recipient of his magical, hideous white fire. He was unconfident, he had qualms of fear.

"Did he hurt you?" he asked.

"No," she said.

"He's an insensible beast," he said, turning his face away.

They came to the little court, which was shut in by old red walls in whose crevices wallflowers were growing. The grass was soft and fine and old, a level floor carpeting the court, the sky was blue overhead. Gerald tossed the rabbit down. It crouched still and would not move. Gudrun watched it with faint horror.

"Why doesn't it move?" she cried.

"It's skulking," he said.

She looked up at him, and a slight sinister smile contracted her white face.

"Isn't it a fool!" she cried. "Isn't it a sickening fool!" The vindictive mockery in her voice made his brain quiver. Glancing up at him, into his eyes, she revealed again the mocking, white-cruel recognition. There was a league between them, abhorrent to them both. They were implicated with each other in abhorrent mysteries.

"How many scratches have you?" he asked, showing his hard forearm, white and hard and torn in red gashes.

"How really vile!" she cried, flushing with a sinister vision. "Mine is nothing."

She lifted her arm and showed a deep red score down the silken white flesh.

"What a devil!" he exclaimed. But it was as if he had had knowledge of her in the long red rent of her forearm, so silken and soft. He did not want to touch her. He would have to make himself touch her, deliberately. The long, shallow red rip seemed torn across his own brain, tearing the surface of his ultimate conscious-ness, letting through the for ever unconscious, unthinkable red ether of the beyond, the obscene beyond.

"It doesn't hurt very much, does it?" he asked, solicitous.

"Not at all," she cried.

And suddenly the rabbit, which had been crouching as if it were a flower, so still and soft, suddenly burst into life. Round and round the court it went, as if shot from a gun, round and round like a furry meteorite, in a tense hard circle that seemed to bind their brains. They all stood in amazement, smiling uncannily, as if the rabbit were obeying some unknown incantation. Round and round it flew, on the grass under the old red walls like a storm.

And then quite suddenly it settled down, hobbled among the grass, and sat considering, its nose twitching like a bit of fluff in the wind. After having considered for a few minutes, a soft bunch with a black, open eye, which perhaps was looking at them, perhaps was not, it hobbled calmly forward and began to nibble the grass with that mean motion of a rabbit's quick eating.

"It's mad," said Gudrun. "It is most decidedly mad."

He laughed.

"The question is," he said, "what is madness? I don't suppose it is rabbit-mad."

"Don't you think it is?" she asked.

"No. That's what it is to be a rabbit."

There was a queer, faint, obscene smile over his face. She looked at him and saw him, and knew that he was initiate as she was initiate. This thwarted her, and contravened her, for the moment.

"God be praised we aren't rabbits," she said in a high, shrill voice.

The smile intensified a little on his face.

"Not rabbits?" he said, looking at her fixedly.

Slowly her face relaxed into a smile of obscene recognition.

"Ah, Gerald," she said in a strong, slow, almost man-like way. " – All that, and more." Her eyes looked up at him with shocking nonchalance.

He felt again as if she had hit him across the face – or rather as if she had torn him across the breast, dully, finally. He turned aside.

"Eat, eat, my darling!" Winifred was softly conjuring the rabbit, and creeping forward to touch it. It hobbled away from her. "Let its mother stroke its fur then, darling, because it is so mysterious – "

D.H. Lawrence from Women in Love

The Hare and the Hedgehog

This story, my dear young folks, seems to be false, but it really is true, for my grandfather, from whom I have it, used always, when relating it, to say: "It must be true, my son, or else no one could tell it to you." The story is as follows. One Sunday morning about harvest time, just as the buckwheat was in bloom, the sun was shining brightly in heaven, the east wind was blowing warmly over the stubble-fields, the larks were singing in the air, the bees buzzing among the buckwheat, the people in their Sunday clothes were all going to church, and all creatures were happy, and the hedgehog was happy too.

The hedgehog, however, was standing by his door with his arms akimbo, enjoying the morning breezes, and slowly trilling a little song to himself, which was neither better nor worse than the songs which hedgehogs are in the habit of singing on a blessed Sunday morning. Whilst he was thus singing half aloud to himself, it suddenly occurred to him that, while his wife was washing and drying the children, he might very well take a walk into the field, and see how his turnips were getting on. The turnips, in fact, were close beside his house, and he and his family were accustomed to eat them, for which reason he looked upon them as his own. No sooner said than done. The hedgehog shut the house-door behind him, and took the path to the field. He had not gone very far from home, and was just turning round the sloe-bush which stands there outside the field, to go up into the turnip-field, when he observed the hare who had gone out on business of the same kind, namely, to visit his cabbages. When the hedgehog caught sight of the hare, he bade him a friendly good morning. But the hare, who was in his own way a distinguished gentleman, and frightfully haughty, did not return the hedgehog's greeting, but said to him, assuming at the same time a very contemptuous manner: "How do you happen to be running about here in the field so early in the morning?" "I am taking a walk," said the hedgehog. "A walk!" said the hare, with a smile. "It seems to me that you might use your legs for a better purpose." This answer made the hedgehog furiously angry, for he can bear anything but a reference to his legs, just because they are crooked by nature. So now the hedgehog said to the hare: "You seem to imagine that you can do more with your legs than I with mine." "That is just what I do think," said the hare. "That can be put to the test," said the hedgehog. "I wager that if we run a race, I will outstrip you." "That is ridiculous! You with your short legs!" said the hare, "but for my part I am willing, if you have such a monstrous fancy for it. What shall we wager?" "A golden louis-d'or and a bottle of brandy," said the

hedgehog. "Done," said the hare. "Shake hands on it, and then we may as well begin at once." "Nay," said the hedgehog, "there is no such great hurry! I am still fasting, I will go home first, and have a little breakfast. In half-an-hour I will be back again at this place."

Hereupon the hedgehog departed, for the hare was quite satisfied with this. On his way the hedgehog thought to himself: "The hare relies on his long legs, but I will contrive to get the better of him. He may be a great man, but he is a very silly fellow, and he shall pay for what he has said." So when the hedgehog reached home, he said to his wife: "Wife, dress yourself quickly, you must go out to the field with me." "What is going on, then?" said his wife. "I have made a wager with the hare, for a gold louis-d'or and a bottle of brandy. I am to run a race with him, and you must be present." "Good heavens, husband," the wife now cried, "are you not right in your mind, have you completely lost your wits? What can make you want to run a race with the hare?" "Hold your tongue, woman," said the hedgehog, "that is my affair. Don't begin to discuss things which are matters for men. Be off, dress yourself, and come with me." What could the hedgehog's wife do? She was forced to obey him, whether she liked it or not.

So when they had set out on their way together, the hedgehog said to his wife: "Now pay attention to what I am going to say. Look you, I will make the long field our race-course. The hare shall run in one furrow, and I in another, and we will begin to run from the top. Now all that you have to do is to place yourself here below in the furrow, and when the hare arrives at the end of the furrow on the other side of you, you must cry out to him: 'I am here already!' "

Then they reached the field, and the hedgehog showed his wife her place, and then walked up the field. When he reached the top, the hare was already there. "Shall we start?" said the hare. "Certainly," said the hedgehog. "Then both at once." So saying, each placed himself in his own furrow. The hare counted: "Once, twice, thrice, and away!" and went off like a whirlwind down the field. The hedgehog, however, only ran about three paces, and then he crouched down in the furrow, and stayed quietly where he was.

When the hare therefore arrived at full speed at the lower end of the field, the hedgehog's wife met him with the cry: "I am here already!" The hare was shocked and wondered not a little, he thought no other than that it was the hedgehog himself who was calling to him, for the hedgehog's wife looked just like her husband. The hare, however, thought to himself: "That has not been done fairly," and cried: "It must be run again, let us have it again." And once more he went off like the wind in a storm, so that he seemed to fly. But the hedgehog's wife stayed quietly in her place. So when the hare reached the top of the field, the hedgehog

himself cried out to him: "I am here already." The hare, however, quite beside himself with anger, cried: "It must be run again, we must have it again." "All right," answered the hedgehog, "for my part we'll run as often as you choose." So the hare ran seventy-three times more, and the hedgehog always held out against him, and every time the hare reached either the top or the bottom, either the hedgehog or his wife said: "I am here already."

At the seventy-fourth time, however, the hare could no longer reach the end. In the middle of the field he fell to the ground, blood streamed out of his mouth, and he lay dead on the spot. But the hedgehog took the louis-d'or which he had won and the bottle of brandy, called his wife out of the furrow, and both went home together in great delight, and if they are not dead, they are living there still.

This is how it happened that the hedgehog made the hare run races with him on the Heath of Buxtehude till he died, and since that time no hare has ever had any fancy for running races with a Buxtehude hedgehog.

The moral of this story is, firstly, that no one, however great he may be, should permit himself to jest at any one beneath him, even if he be only a hedgehog. And, secondly, it teaches, that when a man marries, he should take a wife in his own position, who looks just as he himself looks. So whosoever is a hedgehog let him see to it that his wife is a hedgehog also, and so forth.

The Brothers Grimm

Canine Capers

The rabbit has an evil mind,
Although he looks so good and kind,
His life is a complete disgrace,
Although he has so soft a face.
I hardly like to let you know
How far his wickedness will go.
Enough, if this poor rhyme declares
His fearful cruelty to hares.
He does his very best to keep
These gentle animals from sleep,
By joining in with noisy throngs
Of rabbits singing ribald songs.
To wake their fears and make them hound,
He simulates the Basset-hound.
And if he meets them after dark,
He imitates the greyhound's bark.

Anonymous

A Plague of Rabbits

In New Zealand the rabbit plague began at Bluff. The man who introduced the rabbit there was banqueted and lauded; but they would hang him, now, if they could get him. In England the natural enemy of the rabbit is detested and persecuted; in the Bluff region the natural enemy of the rabbit is honored, and his person is sacred. The rabbit's natural enemy in England is the poacher; in Bluff its natural enemy is the stoat, the weasel, the ferret, the cat, and the mongoose. In England any person below the Heir who is caught with a rabbit in his possession must satisfactorily explain how it got there, or he will suffer fine and imprisonment, together with extinction of his peerage; in Bluff, the cat found with a rabbit in its possession does not have to explain – everybody looks the other way; the person caught noticing would suffer fine and imprisonment, with extinction of peerage. This is a sure way to undermine the moral fabric of a cat. Thirty years from now there will not be a moral cat in New Zealand. Some think there is none there now. In England the poacher is watched, tracked, hunted – he dare not show his face; in Bluff the cat, the weasel, the stoat, and the mongoose go up and down, whither they will, unmolested. By a law of the legislature, posted where all may read, it is decreed that any person found in possession of one of these creatures (dead) must satisfactorily explain the circumstances or pay a fine of not less than five pounds, nor more than twenty pounds. The revenue from this source is not large. Persons who want to pay a hundred dollars for a dead cat are getting rarer and rarer every day. This is bad, for the revenue was to go to the endowment of a university. All governments are more or less short-sighted: in England they fine a poacher, whereas he ought to be banished to New Zealand. New Zealand would pay his way, and give him wages.

Mark Twain

How the Hare Learned to Swim

Sungura, the hare, lived near a river. On his side of the river the grass was dry, but on the opposite bank a clear stream ran into the larger channel and there were green trees and tender grass. How Sungura longed to get across that river, but the tiny hare couldn't swim. Day after day Sungura looked longingly at the other bank and wished he could find a way to get to the opposite side.

It happened that there lived nearby a large family of elephants. Sungura had frequently seen them crossing the river. They waded through with their backs high and dry above the water. How he envied them. I only wish I were as big as an elephant, thought the hare. Then on second thought, he wondered if that would be so nice after all. Elephants couldn't curl up and sleep comfortably in a cool hollow under a log, nor could they hide in the tall grass.

One day the elephants came down to the river bank very close to Sungura's burrow. He watched them closely as they lumbered toward the water swinging their snaky long noses in front of them. Then he had an idea. Cautiously he approached the largest of the beasts, who was carrying a leather bag on his back, and asked politely, "Oh, great Tembo, king of the bushland, would you be so kind as to do a favor for a humble creature like me?"

The elephant, startled to be addressed by someone so far below on the ground, looked with his tiny nearsighted eyes for the speaker. "Oh, it's you Sungura," he said, "and what would you like?"

"Please, most honored Tembo, I should like a ride on your back to the other side of the river."

"Is that all? I see no reason why that can't be arranged. Come over here and sit on my trunk and I will hoist you up beside my bag of honey." The elephant swung his trunk down so that the hare could climb into the curve he made at the end and with a swish he swung it around and put Sungura down on his broad back beside the honey.

"Oh," gasped the hare, "what a wonderful ride."

"Now sit quietly my friend, and you shall have another ride even more wonderful." Tembo stepped into the water, followed by his family. Sungura, in delight, sat securely on top.

When they were out into the water Sungura looked closely at the honey bag, sticky on the outside. The hare licked a few drops from the outside – "Mmmmm – good," he whispered. Then he carefully opened the top of the bag and took just a little lick, then a little more and a little more, until he had eaten every bit of the honey! He dropped a little on Tembo's back. "What do I feel?" asked the elephant.

"Only tears of joy and gratitude, most honored Tembo; my tears because I am so happy," answered Sungura.

"Only too glad to help," said Tembo as he splashed on across the stream.

Just as they reached the opposite bank Sungura said to the elephant, "Oh, kind sir, there are many large birds here. I am afraid of them. Will you please give me some stones to throw so that I may frighten them away."

The obliging Tembo picked up some small stones with his trunk and handed them up. "There you are. Those should be just right."

"Thank you, great Tembo. You are very kind."

Sungura threw only a few of the stones. The rest he put into the honey bag. Then he asked to be set down.

Swish, he rode the elephant's trunk to the ground, and scurried away into the grass.

Tembo and his family went on down the trail to their meadow. When the big elephant reached up and brought down the honey bag from his back, he was startled to find that the honey had turned to lumps. Then he opened the bag and found stones – nothing but stones! He cried out in anger and when the other elephants came to see what was wrong he said, "That ungrateful hare!

Look what he did after I had befriended him. He left me stones for my honey."

Many days later when Sungura was happily eating some new shoots of tender grass at the water's edge, Tembo came swaying silently out of the woods. The hare didn't see him until he spoke. "Good day, Sungura, and how do you like your new home?"

Startled, the hare replied, "Oh, kind sir, I – I – I." His voice trailed off into nothing.

"Perhaps you'd like another ride on my back," suggested Tembo.

Sungura was puzzled by the generosity of the big elephant, but the tantalizing prospect of another ride overcame his desire to run away. "Oh, yes sir, if you'd be so kind, sir," he said.

With a great flourish Tembo swung his trunk to the ground and picked up the hare. With a tremendous swish, the elephant swung Sungura around and threw him – splash – far out into the river. Down went the hare – up he came spluttering and gasping, "Help – help – I can't swim."

"Time you learned," said the

elephant with a chuckle.

Round and round bobbed Sungura, struggling and kicking and finally swimming uncertainly to the bank. Out he crawled, wet and shaking.

In the distance he heard the rumbling laugh of Tembo. "Next time you try to trick me, remember I have a good memory."

Sungura learned more than gratitude from his thorough dunking in the river. He learned how to swim.

An East-African Legend

Four-Footed Beasts

Rabbits and Hares enjoy remarkable fecundity
and display curious sexual and
social habits. But no less
extraordinary, as observers such
as Claudius Aelianus and Edward
Topsell have noted, are their
amazing physical attributes.

Of Matters Coital

Hares copulate in the rearward position, as I have already stated, since they are retromingent animals: they pair and bring forth at all seasons. Superfetation occurs during pregnancy, and they bring forth every month. The young are not produced all together, but at intervals of as many days as it may happen to be. The female has milk before parturition, and after bearing will have intercourse immediately; she conceives while still suckling her young. In consistency the milk is similar to the sow's. The young are born blind, as are the young of most of the fissiped animals. . . .

The rabbit. . . is abundant in semen. This is shown by its hairiness. It has an excessive amount of hair; indeed, it has hair under the feet and inside the jaws, and is the only animal which does so. This hairiness is a sign that it has a large amount of residue; and for this same reason, too, men that are hairy are more prone to sexual intercourse and have more semen than men that are smooth. As for the hare, often some of its fetations are imperfect; others of its offspring, however, it brings to birth in a perfected state.

Aristotle

Hermaphroditic Hares

I have heard from one who is a hunter and a good man besides, the kind that would not tell a lie, a story which I believe to be true and shall therefore relate. For he used to maintain that even the male hare does, in fact, give birth and produce offspring and endure the birthpangs and partake of both sexes. And he told me how it bears and rears its young ones, and how it brings perhaps two or three to birth; and he bore witness to this too, and then as the finishing touch to the whole story added the following: a male hare had been caught in a half-dead state, and its belly was enlarged, being pregnant. Now he admitted that it had been cut open and that its womb, containing three leverets, had been discovered. These, he said, which so far were undisturbed, were taken out and lay there like lifeless flesh. When, however, they were warmed by the sun and had spent some time slowly

acquiring a little heat, they came to themselves and revived, and one of them, I suppose, stirred and looked up and presently put out its tongue as well and opened its mouth in its craving for nourishment. Accordingly some milk was brought, as was proper for such young creatures, and little by little they were reared up, to furnish (in my opinion) an astonishing proof of their birth by a male. I cannot prevail upon myself to doubt the story, the reason being that the narrator's tongue was a stranger to falsehoods and exaggeration.

Claudius Aelianus

Rabbits' Sexual Habits

Rabbits have no marriage laws as such; but in their sexual relations buck and doe are tied to each other by a code of behaviour closely resembling that of man. Young rabbits play together innocently, like children, at first; then comes an adolescent period, with indiscriminate sexual pursuits without fertile mating – resembling those of young men and women. The young couple eventually settle in a burrow, often a poor one, but they will improve it, or move to a better one as their social standing in the community rises. The young woman is "married" now, the young doe is a "queen." Under fair conditions, without severe pressures due to predators, over-population, or food shortages, the couple – human or rabbit – may remain united for the rest of their lives by their territorial allegiance to a home. If there is a surplus female or two around, the queen doe will not actively prevent the king having sexual relations with her or them, provided these secondary females do not enter her home, and she will only attack them if they obstruct her path when grazing near by; married man has a similar relationship, albeit more furtive and clandestine, if he takes a "mistress." But neither man nor buck will usually allow another male to approach his female sexually, if he can prevent it. He will fight for the sanctity of home, where the female provides the main bonds tying the male to a husbandly existence – warm, dry quarters and sexual satisfaction. In man, family "togetherness" is also important, and it is tolerated by the father rabbit in much the same degree. Provided the young ones are docile they are welcome to stay at home and be treated affectionately as subordinate beings.

Rabbits are so human. Or is it the other way round – humans are so rabbit?

Ronald M. Lockley

What's the Difference?

In form of body, the Rabbit is rounder and plumper than the Hare, and the flanks are less contracted, while the proportionately shorter ears and limbs give it a much more ordinary appearance. . . . In weight, a wild Rabbit usually varies from between two-and-a-half and three pounds, but specimens which have turned the scale at five pounds are on record. . . .

As regards the general external form of the Hare . . . the body is large, compressed, and deep; the neck very short; the head of moderate size, convex above, and broad and obtuse at the muzzle, with a depressed nose, and the upper lip tumid and divided by a vertical median cleft. The laterally placed eyes are large and remarkably prominent; and the long ears are narrow, deeply concave, and rounded at the tips. The somewhat long claws are slightly curved, compressed, and rather sharp; although on the hind-feet they become blunted in old animals. The fur, as in the other members of the genus, consists of two kinds of hairs, of which the one is long and coarse, and the other short, fine, and somewhat woolly. In addition to the usual "whiskers," a few long bristly hairs are situated over each eye.

From Lloyd's Natural History, *1896*

The Rabbit-Warren

A Rabbit-warren presents towards evening a curious and not uninteresting spectacle. The ground everywhere pierced with deep and tortuous holes, the absence of all esculent vegetation around it, and the playful gambols and rapid retreat of the inhabitants, as they either sport in security or fly from the approach of danger, are circumstances which at once indicate the peculiar habits of the species and present a lively and amusing scene.

Thomas Bell

The Four-Footed Beast

Whatfoeuer beaft be borne in your flocke, hauing that marke vpon them, which is commonly called hares-tooth, neuer fuffer them to fucke their dam, but caft them awaie as vnprofitable and Baftard cattell; the necke of a hare is long, fmall, round, foft, and flexible, the fhoulder-bone ftraight and broad, for her more eafieturning, her legges before foft and found, ftanding a little afunder very flexible, broder behind then before, and the hinder legges longer then the former, a breaft not narrowe, but fitted to take breath in courfe, a nimble backe and flefhy belly, tender loines, hollow fides, fat buttockes filled vp, comely, ftrong and neruyloines, the forefeet very flexible, onely it wanteth a com-modious taile for courfe. The eies are browne, it is a fubtil beaft, but not bold, it fildome looketh forward, becaufe it goeth by iumpes. The eie-lids comming from the brows, are too fhort to couer their eies, and therefore this fence is very weake in them, and befides their ouermuch fleepe, their feare of Dogges and fwiftneffe, caufeth them to fee the leffe; when they Watch they fhut their eies, and when they fleep they open them. . . .

They are deceiued which deliuer by authority of holy Scriptures that hares loue to lodge them vpon rocks, but we haue manifefted elfe-where, that thofe places are to bee vnderftood of Conies. They haue fore-knowledge both of wind and weather, Summer and Winter by their nofes, for in the Winter they make their formes in the Sun-fhine, becaufe they canot abide froft and cold, and in the Summer they reft toward the North, remaining in fome higher ground where they receiue colder ayre.

We haue fhewed already that their fight is dimm, but yet heerin it is true that *Plutarch* faith, they haue *Vifum indefeffum*, an indefattigable fence of feeing, fo that the continuance in a meane degree, counteruaileth in them the want of excellency. Their hearing is moft pregnant, for the Egyptians when they fignifie hearing picture a hare, and for this caufe we haue fhewed you already that their eares are long like hornes, their voyce is a whyning voice, and therefore Authors call it *Vagitum*, as they doe a yong childs. . . .

They reft in the day time, and walk abroad to feed in the night, neuer feeding near home, either becaufe they are delighted with forren foode, or elfe becaufe they woulde exercife their legs in going, or elfe by fecret inftinct of nature, to conceale their forms and lodging places vnknowne, their hart and blood is colde, which *Albertus* affigneth for a caufe of their night-feeding: they eat alfo grapes, and when they are ouercome with heat, they eat of an herbe called *Lacfuca Leporina*, and of the *Romaines* and *Hetrurians*, *Ciferbita*, of the *Venetians*, *Lacfucinos*, of the French *Lacferones*, that is, hares Lettuce, hares houfe, hares pallace, and there

is no difeafe in this beaft the cure whereof fhe doth not feeke for in this hearbe. Hares are faid to chew the cud in the holy Scripture, they neuer drinke, but content themfelues with the dew, and for that caufe they often fal rotten. It is reported by *Phillippus Belot*, that when a hare drunke Wine Fhee inftantly died, they render their Vrine backwards, and their milke is a thicke as a Swines, and of all creatures they haue milke in vdders before they deliuer their young.

Edward Topsell, 1607

The Treatment of Hares

In the year 1774, being much indisposed both in mind and body, incapable of diverting myself either with company or books, and yet in a condition that made some diversion necessary, I was glad of any thing that would engage my attention, without fatiguing it. The children of a neighbour of mine had a leveret given them for a plaything; it was at that time about three months old. Understanding better how to tease the poor creature than to feed it, and soon becoming weary of their charge, they readily consented that their father, who saw it pining and growing leaner every day, should offer it to my acceptance. I was willing enough to take the prisoner under my protection, perceiving that, in the management of such an animal, and in the attempt to tame it, I should find just that sort of employment which my case required. It was soon known among the neighbours that I was pleased with the present, and the consequence was, that in a short time I had as many leverets offered to me as would have stocked a paddock. I undertook the care of three, which it is necessary that I should here distinguish by the names I gave them – Puss, Tiney, and Bess. Notwithstanding the two feminine appellatives, I must inform you, that they were all males. Immediately commencing carpenter, I built them houses to sleep in; each had a separate apartment, so contrived that their ordure would pass through the bottom of it; an earthen pan placed under each received whatsoever fell which being duly emptied and washed, they were thus kept perfectly sweet and clean. In the daytime they had the range of a hall, and at night retired each to his own bed, never intruding into that of another.

Puss grew presently familiar, would leap into my lap, raise himself

upon his hinder feet, and bite the hair from my temples. He would suffer me to take him up, and to carry him about in my arms, and has more than once fallen fast asleep upon my knee. He was ill three days, during which time I nursed him, kept him apart from his fellows, that they might not molest him, (for, like many other wild animals, they persecute one of their own species that is sick), and by constant care, and trying him with a variety of herbs, restored him to perfect health. No creature could be more grateful than my patient after his recovery; a sentiment which he most significantly expressed by licking my hand, first the back of it, then the palm, then every finger separately, then between all the fingers, as if anxious to leave no part of it unsaluted; a ceremony which he never performed but once again upon a similar occasion. Finding him extremely tractable, I made it my custom to carry him always after breakfast into the garden, where he hid himself generally under the leaves of a cucumber vine, sleeping or chewing the cud till evening; in the leaves also of that vine he found a favourite repast. I had not long habituated him to this taste of liberty, before he began to be impatient for the return of the time when he might enjoy it. He would invite me to the garden by drumming upon my knee, and by a look of such expression, as it was not possible to misinterpret. If this rhetoric did not immediately succeed, he would take the skirt of my coat between his teeth, and pull it with all his force. Thus Puss might be said to be perfectly tamed, the shyness of his nature was done away, and on the whole it was visible by many symptoms, which I have not room to enumerate, that he was happier in human society than when shut up with his natural companions.

Not so Tiney; upon him the kindest treatment had not the least effect. He too was sick, and in his sickness had an equal share of my attention; but if after his recovery I took the liberty to stroke him, he would grunt, strike with his fore feet, spring forward, and bite. He was however

very entertaining in his way; even his
surliness was a matter of mirth, and
in his play he preserved such an air
of gravity, and performed his feats
with such a solemnity of manner, that
in him too I had an agreeable com-
panion.

Bess, who died soon after he was
full grown, and whose death was
occasioned by his being turned into
his box, which had been washed,
while it was yet damp, was a hare of
great humour and drollery. Puss was
tamed by gentle usage; Tiney was not
to be tamed at all; and Bess had a
courage and confidence that made
him tame from the beginning. I
always admitted them into the par-
lour after supper, when the carpet
affording their feet a firm hold, they
would frisk, and bound, and play a
thousand gambols, in which Bess,
being remarkably strong and fearless,
was always superior to the rest, and
proved himself the Vestris of the
party. One evening the cat, being in
the room, had the hardiness to pat
Bess upon the cheek, an indignity to
which he resented by drumming

upon her back with such violence
that the cat was happy to escape
from under his paws, and hide herself.

I describe these animals as having
each a character of his own. Such
they were in fact, and their countenances were so expressive of that
character, that, when I looked only
on the face of either, I immediately
knew which it was. It is said that a
shepherd, however numerous his
flock, soon becomes so familiar with
their features, that he can, by that
indication only, distinguish each
from all the rest; and yet, to a common observer, the difference is
hardly perceptible. I doubt not that
the same discrimination in the cast of
countenances would be discoverable
in hares, and am persuaded that
among a thousand of them no two
could be found exactly similar; a cir-
cumstance little suspected by those
who have not had opportunity to
observe it. These creatures have a
singular sagacity in discovering the
minutest alteration that is made in
the place to which they are accus-

tomed, and instantly apply their nose to the examination of a new object. A small hole being burnt in the carpet, it was mended with a patch, and that patch in a moment underwent the strictest scrutiny. They seem too to be very much directed by the smell in the choice of their favourites: to some persons, though they saw them daily, they could never be reconciled, and would even scream when they attempted to touch them; but a miller coming in engaged their affections at once; his powdered coat had charms that were irresistible. It is no wonder that my intimate acquaintance with these specimens of the kind has taught me to hold the sportsman's amusement in abhorrence; he little knows what amiable creatures he persecutes, of what gratitude they are capable, how cheerful they are in their spirits, what enjoyment they have of life, and that, impressed as they seem with a peculiar dread of man, it is only because man gives them peculiar cause for it. . . .

Bess, I have said, died young; Tiney lived to be nine years old, and died at last, I have reason to think, of some hurt in his loins by a fall; Puss is still living, and has just completed his tenth year, discovering no signs of decay, nor even of age, except that he has grown more discreet and less frolicsome than he was. I cannot conclude without observing, that I have lately introduced a dog to his acquaintance, a spaniel that had never seen a hare to a hare that had never seen a spaniel. I did it with great caution, but there was no real need of it. Puss discovered no token of fear, nor Marquis the least symptom of hostility. There is therefore, it should seem, no natural antipathy between dog and hare, but the pursuit of the one occasions the flight of the other, and the dog pursues because he is trained to it; they eat bread at the same time out of the same hand, and are in all respects sociable and friendly.

I should not do complete justice to my subject, did I not add, that they have no ill scent belonging to them, that they are indefatigably nice in keeping themselves clean, for which purpose nature has furnished them with a brush under each foot; and that they are never infested by any vermin.

    May 28, 1784.

William Cowper

Memorandum Found Among Mr. Cowper's Papers

Tuesday, March 9, 1786.
This day died poor Puss, aged eleven years eleven months. He died between twelve and one at noon, of mere old age, and apparently without pain.

The Mind of a Rabbit

A warm June afternoon. From the shelf built amid the fluttering green leaves of the elm tree the observer could watch, unobserved himself, the first stirrings of the warren. It was a pleasant scene. The beautiful parkland thick with summer flowers, radiant with cowslips, comfrey, meadowsweet and bugle, wide open to the sun retreating from the zenith. Ringdoves cooed in the surrounding woods; and were answered by the cool, staccato notes of a songthrush from the young beeches, and the liquid complaining notes of the robin.

The first rabbit to appear was a large buck with scarred ears. He emerged from the central warren, sat up, gazed round for a moment, then began to groom his coat. He licked the pads of his forepaws as he held them upturned, coating them with saliva, then pressed them down together over the sides of his face.

He washed his ears by pulling each down in turn with the wet brushes of his forepaws. He washed both sides of his body with his tongue. He licked and cleaned the fur beneath his feet. This was the typical toilet of a healthy rabbit.

Suddenly he became perfectly still. He was gazing at a large hawk which had at that moment alighted silently on a fence post six feet high and thirty yards away.

The two creatures – ancient enemies; buzzard and rabbit, predator and prey – stared at each other for a long time. What went on in the mind of each? Why did both become so still? Was it due to instinct or learning (discernment), this reaction of stillness?...Surely there was some reasoning at work in both animals – they were not just automatons, as some observers of animal behavior would have us believe.

An "instinctive fear" is said to assail man when an unexpected noise, a brutal crash, or alternatively the silent surprise visit of an enemy, occurs. Our instinct is to become rigid, ready to escape, to flee, hair rising on the nape of the neck while our shocked, numbed senses presently inform us – if we are not too terrified to think – of the true nature of the disturbance, acceptable or evil.

Much the same reaction, the same instinctive fear, alarms the senses of the wild animal. All its waking hours it is subject to these alarms in its world where life is cheap and expendable, and to survive one must remain alert to each movement in the environment. But just as the human brain becomes used to and ignores the ticking of the clock, the sound and sight of traffic or of rain, the animal becomes used to and ignores those sounds and sights which do not harm: the wind in the leaves, the songs of birds, the whir-ring of insects.

Probably both bird and rabbit were of the same age; the buck by the numbered tag in his ear I knew to be twenty-four months old, that is middle-aged or at least old enough to be sure of himself, and complacently able in his home environment to stare his enemy in the eye. I wondered what was going on within that tough skull, what processes of thought stirred the nerves in the grey matter of a brain which, weight for weight, was possibly twice as heavy as the brain of the hawk which glared so piercingly at the rabbit.

Both possessed large eyes, adapted to their special requirements of seeing movement over long distances, and in the dusk. In addition the rabbit had huge mobile ears which could be orientated to register and amplify all fine sounds of the moment from any direction. The buzzard was not deaf either, but its ears were small, hidden in its head feathers, and doubtless its hearing was weaker than that of the rabbit.

To understand the mind of an animal one needs at least some knowledge of the physiology of the senses of the living creature. To begin with impressions of sight, what did the buzzard see, and what was the image in the eye of the rabbit? And how near are these perceptions to those of the human observer? Not as near as Beatrix Potter's caricatures of rabbits would suggest, but perhaps nearer than the sceptics suppose.

The basic structure of the eye in bird and rabbit and human is the same: the image made by the lens falls on the nerve cells of the retina, causing a physical, chemical reaction which flashes an impulse over the nerve fibres to the brain. It is discovered that most mammals are colour blind, especially the crepuscular and nocturnal species; but birds in general have colour vision, otherwise there would be no meaning to their often brilliant plumages: and their eyes have a considerable acuity which gives them a telescopic power to see small objects clearly at a much greater distance than we can.

Probably the rabbit saw the buzzard in subdued black and white tones – and none too sharply. The bird blended into a background of trees and plants of the same black and white shades, and would be difficult to distinguish once the rabbit had looked away and lost the image, provided the bird did not move again.

The buzzard remained perfectly still on the post; the rabbit looked away losing interest, losing the image of its enemy; and, bending down, began to graze with sweeping left and right movements of its jaws.

Very soon the buzzard turned its head to watch – with colour vision – the flight of a wood pigeon across the paddock. Experience had taught the bird that a full-grown rabbit was too powerful and difficult to tackle and kill, especially right out in the open.

As for the buck, he had not moved his head to look up at the noisy-

winged pigeon, but had paused to listen, then quickly resumed his grazing. The movement of the pigeon induced reaction: on the rabbit's part a swift assessment of possible danger of attack, and on the buzzard's part an appraisal of the movement as a source of food, of killing prey, but perhaps also of possible attack by the enemies of the buzzard – man, raven, rival bird.

Without turning its head, the rabbit had directed its ears forward to catch the sounds of wing-beats, while its wide-spaced eyes, with their side and forward stereoscopic vision, saw all around in an arc of more than 180 degrees: recognizing no danger in the familiar pigeon, it continued its grazing.

The buzzard, with forward directed vision, possibly of less than 180 degrees, was obliged to move its head to follow the flighting pigeon. This movement of the buzzard, though slight, was probably detected by the rabbit, which depends for survival on the ability to detect movement. But it took no further action in respect of the birds; they were not near, nor coming near enough to surprise him. He continued to feed. So the zebra of the African plains turns from the sight of its enemy, the lion, at a short but safe distance, and resumes grazing. So man reads a newspaper, beside a road along which traffic roars at fifty miles an hour. Rabbit, zebra, man are aware of safety distances and keep them.

The rabbit was living, keeping alive by two processes: eating to nourish itself, and avoiding being eaten by maintaining a safe distance from a death-dealing predator. Man is a rabbit, a zebra in habit, and consciously and subconsciously engages much of his life in the same situation, of eating to live, of avoiding death from many and numerous sources, such as war and disease, and being killed by his enemies or by the machinery which he himself has invented.

Ronald M. Lockley

CHAPTER FIVE

Of Prophecy and Superstition

Apparently feet aren't the only
charmed parts of rabbits' and hares'
anatomy. Hare-skin garters
induce swiftness in the wearer;
burning hare fat prompts scandalous
behavior in both men and women;
rabbit rennet taken as a beverage
prevents pregnancy. And the
rabbit as a whole makes an
enchantingly delicious stew.

For the Love of Peter

• A lamp of hare's fat set in a room
and left to burn will cause the gen-
tlemen and ladies to throw off all
their clothes quickly and begin to
laugh, dance and sing, as long as the
lamp burns. It is said that the furi-
ous and scandalous orgies of the
times of the Borgias in Italy were
brought about by this charm, the
walls of the palace echoing to
demoniac laughter, while beautiful
women and even old men dis-
ported themselves in the dim light
like elves and gnomes.

• To break love tokens, send the gift
back to the giver and wear a rabbit's foot, namely, the left hind foot
of a graveyard rabbit.

• If a rabbit runs across the path in
front of you a certain number of
times, that will be the number of
years until you get married.

• On the first day of the month say,
"Rabbit! Rabbit! Rabbit!" and the
first thing you know, you'll get a
present from someone you like
very much.

Rabbit Luck

- If cold chills run down your spine, a rabbit is running over your grave.
- A rabbit's foot in your pocket will keep away ghosts.
- The appearance of a white hare predicts a storm to the Cornish people.
- If the young men of the parish catch a hare and bring it to the parson by ten o'clock on Easter Monday, the parson will give them a calf's head, a hundred eggs and a groat in money.
- To find a hare on a May morning is an evil omen, and the hare should be stoned.
- If you see a hare run along the street of a village, there will soon be a fire.
- If a hare crosses your road, if out on business, you'll have no success.
- It is unlucky if a hare runs across the road of a Roman; he will be robbed or some mischance will happen to him before he gets home.

Galloping Garters

Gather some of the herb called motherwort, when the sun
is entering the first degree of the sign of Capricorn:
let it dry a little in the shade, and make some garters
of the skin of a young hare; that is to say, having cut
the skin of the hare into strips two inches wide, double
them, sew the before-mentioned herb between, and wear them
on your legs. No horse can long keep up with a man on
foot who is furnished with those garters.

From Natural History Lore and Legend, *1895*

Pregnant Superstitions

- If a woman about to become a mother sees the little white tuft on the end of a hare's tail, the little one will have a harelip. She may avert the danger by unraveling a small portion of the seam of her petticoat.
- In Sweden there is a superstition that if a pregnant woman should see a hare's head, her child will be born with a harelip. In Scotland it is believed that the same deformity will occur if the mother steps over a hare's body.

- If a woman drinks the rennet of a hare after having completed menstruation she is prevented from becoming pregnant.
- It is unlucky for an expectant mother to see a hare sitting. If it's running, it does no harm.
- If an expectant mother eats rabbit meat, her child will sleep with its eyes open.

Help for Hunters

- A rabbit can be caught in a newly made box if the box is made of old planks and allowed to stand a year.
- Hunt rabbits after the first white frost. They are then fat from eating persimmons and frost.
- When it has snowed, it is a good time to go rabbit hunting.
- If a fisherman meets a hare on his way fishing, he turns back, knowing that his luck is lost for the day.
- If you eat a hare for breakfast, you must hunt overnight.
- If you hunt two hares, you'll lose the one and leave the other.
- If you see a white hare, you'll be unlucky.
- If you see a black hare, good fortune will shine on you.
- To shoot at a rabbit under an elder tree is a very bad omen.
- Some artful dodgers mix the juice of henbane with the blood of a leveret and anoint their gaiters, thinking that all the hares in the neighborhood will be attracted towards the wearers.

Hares to your Health

Thus much will I say as to the commendation of the hare and of the defence of hunter's toyle, that no one beast, be it never so great, is profitable to so many and so diverse uses in Physicke as the hare and partes thereof. For the liver of the hare dryed and made in powder is good for those that be liver sick, and the whole hare, skinne and all, put in an earthen pot close stopped, and baked in an oven so drie that it may be made in powder, being given in white wine, is wonderful good for the stone.

William George Black

- Two hairs from a rabbit's tail and an inch of opossum-tail will secure the possessor from sudden death, if worn in a small bag over the heart.
- The right forefoot of a hare is good to ward off disease.
- The right forefoot of a rabbit is used to ward off rheumatism.
- The anklebone of a hare's foot relieves cramps.
- A rabbit's foot worn around the neck will prevent asthma.
- Rabbit feet worn around your neck will keep off spells.
- Put rabbit tobacco in a corncob pipe and smoke it. Blow the smoke into the ear and it will cure earache.

Rabbit Stew

There was an Old Person whose habits
Induced him to feed upon rabbits;
    When he'd eaten eighteen
    He turned perfectly green,
Upon which he relinquished those habits.

Edward Lear

The flesh of the tame rabbit is very
inferior in flavour to that of the wild,
but the former is more esteemed in
London on account of its greater ten-
derness.

Thomas Bell

I confess that much as I delight in
watching warren-life, and, indebted
as I am to the grotesqueness of rabbits at play or at work for many a
hearty laugh, I remember them very
tenderly in a pie – a cold pie.

Philip Stewart Robinson

An old hare hoar,
And an old hare hoar,
Is very good meat in Lent;
But a hare that is hoar
Is too much for a score,
When it hoars ere it be spent.

William Shakespeare, Romeo and Juliet

Hare is a dish that, in Spain, is
never seen on the table, because
there is a superstition that hares go
in the night to graveyards, dig up the
graves, and eat the dead bodies.

From Encyclopedia of Superstitions,
Folklore, and the Occult Sciences of the
World, *1903*

CHAPTER SIX

Signs of Sorcery

The symbolism, myth and magic of
rabbits and hares have been debated by writers
down through the ages. Only one
indisputable fact emerges from
the controversy: these creatures have always
been, and continue to be, the mystics
of the animal world.

The Easter Hare

The custom of eating the Easter hare is classed by Mr. Elton among those ceremonies which bear most openly the marks of their original paganism. It is best known in Pomerania, where hares are caught at Easter-tide to provide a public meal. In other parts of Germany there are traces of a similar tradition. Thus, the children in South Germany are told that a hare lays the Pasche eggs, and a nest is made for the hare to lay them in; and it is customary in many parts of the country "to place a figure of the hare among the Easter eggs, when given as a present, either a hare in a basket of eggs, or a small figure of a hare in one of the fancy eggs." The same object is common on Easter cards.

From Folk-Lore, *1892*

A Magic Spell

On Thursday, the 4th of April 1621, my eldest son, William Fairfax, being in the field called Birkbanks aforesaid, started a hare out of a bush and set a dog at her. Mr. Smithson, vicar of Fuystone, saw her also, and in like sort caused his dog to run at her, but they quickly lost the sight of her. That day, soon after, the child was in trance, and the strange woman did appear to her and told her that she was the hare which her brother and the vicar set their dogs at; and that she came over the water with her brother, William, and that he should see her again the next time he went to that place; which proved true. Also she affirmed that when she was in likeness of a hare, or of any such thing, she was then senseless. That being said, she showed to the child eight pictures of one sort, by which she said she did bewitch such as she had now in hand. Three of them were of my children, and three of John Jeffray's daughters, the other two she said were one of them a maid, late servant of Ralph Franckland, and the other of a young woman called Atkinson; which two last mentioned (at the same time), were strangely afflicted, especially the man, with trances and swoonings. Also she had her five pictures, by which she said she had practiced before upon others. The child desired to feel the pictures, and the woman did suffer her to handle the first six of them, which she felt to be substantial, not illusory. For the woman's report that she was that hare, the detractors and slanderous scoffers of this infant may be confounded, if they consider that the child foretold out of the woman's mouth that her brother should see the hare again, which he did indeed in the same place upon Tuesday, the 9th of April next following, which foretelling could be no imposture of

the child, for her teachers, if they can suppose any such, could not themselves preface it so many days before. I cannot with silence pass over her saying that being in that or the like shape she was senseless, for as to the transforming of shapes in this kind the question deserveth to be written of in a whole volume, but it is far above my learning to resolve it, and books from which I might borrow any help are (in this wilderness), as rare as civility is, or learning itself.

Edward Fairfax from Daemonologia: A Discourse in Magic

Let There be Lettuce

Among all the Algonkin tribes whose myths have been preserved we find much is said about a certain Giant Rabbit, to whom all sorts of powers were attributed. He was the master of all animals; he was the teacher who first instructed men in the arts of fishing and hunting; he imparted to the Algonkins the mysteries of their religious rites; he taught them picture writing and the interpretation of dreams; nay, far more than that, he was the original ancestor, not only of their nation, but of the whole race of man, and, in fact, was none other than the primal Creator himself, who fashioned the earth and gave life to all that thereon is.

Sir James George Frazer

Hare Signs

The hare, itself defenseless, is a symbol of men who put the hope of their salvation in the Christ and His passion. It is also a well-known symbol of lust and fecundity. A white hare is sometimes placed at the feet of the Virgin Mary to indicate her triumph over lust.

G. Ferguson

When

When I'm on your lawn
you all go quiet
hoping to catch me

I am listening
though still

When you get too close
I take off
stretching myself out
to twice my length

Don't follow or
if you do

prepare to shrink
and tumble to strange dark

Brian Swann

Reverent Rabbit

There was a rabbit
Who had no stairs;
He went down a rope
To say his prayers.

Anonymous

The Rabbit's Foot

The rabbit arouses a great variety of human emotions, provoking every kind of expression from belly laughter to frustration and disgust, as illustrated in many popular games, jingles, and tales. With trickery and finesse he plays his game, apparently without malice toward those that harry him. If pursued by dogs and armed men, he darts about in a zigzag manner; long before the hunters are aware of his maneuvers he manages to get in behind them. Some say he is a devil, a demon, a witch, a ghost, and a perennial glutton who takes more than his due share of the world's food. He can be a delightful pet, but you must remember that he is excessively prolific and he also has power in his punch. His foot is reputed to be a charm that opens many a door to good fortune.

No doubt the rabbit understands how and why he practices his varied behavior. For centuries he has guarded his own security — he and his children have kept their eyes open, their ears erect, their stomach crammed, and their feet ready to leap at a moment's notice towards the nearest hole or thicket. Under stress and strain, this hungry predator has sharpened his manners and made the best of what he has.

Joseph D. Clark

Divine or Degraded?

In an early fifteenth-century tapestry called "Conversation galante dans la verdure," shown by van Marle, a young lady is sitting on a bench in a meadow. She has a dog with her and she is listening to a young gentleman, who is addressing her with some ardor. Around the couple are a number of plump hares. How is the young man making out? The attitudes of the animals provide the answer. The young lady allows the dog to put its front paws on her knees and bury its snout in her lap. Nearby, a hare, although appearing to be running away, turns its face toward the dog with an amiable expression. Since the dog is the pursuing male and the hare is the symbol of woman, our conclusion is that the young man's advances are being welcomed by the lady. Although the hare has various symbolic qualities and might stand, among other things, for timidity, swiftness, blindness, madness, ill-luck, supernatural evil, treachery, and uncleanliness, its value in this illustration is unequivocal. . . .

The symbolism of the hare, whether religious or secular, was almost always pejorative. Exegetical writers declared the hare signifies incontinence; it belonged to the lascivious hunt of Venus, the hunt of lust, rather than to the virtuous hunt. In a vigorous Romanesque sculpture at the twelfth-century Collegiate Church in Königslutter, Lower Saxony, two hares with wide, glaring eyes and gaping mouths prance over a prostrate man whose feet are bound. Like the demons' heads on the apse below them, they appear to symbolize evil. To the bestiarist the double sex of the creature — *aliquando masculus sit, aliquando femina* (sometimes it may be masculine, sometimes feminine) — made the hare a type of the double-minded man. The hare which had once attended Aphrodite on Greek vases, or had been exchanged as a love gage by Greek youths, or had watched the sexual encounters of Poseidon and Amymone, of Nessos and Deianeira, or had merely stood

between the legs of the phallic horse, became the attribute of Lust. In the Albertina at Vienna, Vitorre Pisano's young woman has a startling muscular emaciation, high breasts, long limbs, and a fashionable, snake-like wig. But the hare crouching at her feet reveals that, close as she might come to the standards of a model for *Vogue*, she is simply Luxuria, the symbol of sensual delight. According to popular legend, Aristotle, the venerable Greek savant, became so besotted with an attractive woman that he agreed to become her palfrey and let her ride him. A bas-relief underneath a console on the facade of the cathedral church of Saint-Jeans at Lyons dating from the fifteenth century depicts the philosopher in his humiliating position. Behind him lurks the hare, the symbol of libidinousness.

Beryl Rowland

Nine Rabbits

Albino, Flemish, and Chinchilla, mixed,
nine rabbits flow through poses never fixed.

Nine rabbits, caged concupiscents, insist
that procreation be a public act.
Though wilder rabbits dance by moonlight, these
dismay the orthodox with noonday ease.

Their bland and furry lechings can distract
a casual eye.
Within such lively dust,
a cosmic force devolves to hopping lust:
that force, so changed, gives little rise to mirth.
Close by, in suburbs bordering the zoo,
the people act much as the rabbits do,
and Malthus sleeps in his triumphant earth.

Nine rabbits move through poses never fixed,
Albino, Flemish, and Chinchilla, mixed.

John Bennett

Why Rabbits Jump

"Why are you rabbits jumping so?
Now please tell why, tell why."
"We jump to see the big round moon
Up in the sky, the sky."

Japanese Nursery Rhyme

Moon Myths

The mythical hare is undoubtedly the moon, and the widespread connection of the animal with the luminary gives the myth something of a popular acceptation. Thus the Chinese represent the moon-figure, *Jut-ho*, with a hare at her feet, and symbolize Luna by a rabbit pounding in a mortar. In Vedic myth, "the leaping one" is the moon, and the spots on the face of it are hares by the shore of the moon-lake.

Philip Stewart Robinson

The Private Life of the Rabbit

Why does the rabbit amuse and charm us? Most of us who are not farmers, foresters or occupiers of large gardens, smile indulgently at the sight of the rabbit in meadow, wood, or other wild environment, or in the well-fed confinement of a comfortable hutch. Perhaps the garden-poet, quoted above, may have touched on the reason?

The rabbit has a baby face, of rounded outlines, snub nose, enormous ears and eyes, and an appearance of helplessness. Konrad Lorenz has suggested that it is because of these attributes of infancy, this facial resemblance to the young human, that we – women and children especially – are pleased when we gaze at a rabbit. The fox, with its pointed nose, the badger with its pig-like profile, are less charming, even disliked and feared; we also remember the carnivorous habit of these and other long-nosed animals, and hold this, perhaps also subconsciously, against them. Yet the podgy faces of cub fox and baby badger delight us – again perhaps because of the childish appearance: rounded, helpless, without guile.

The rabbit is vegetarian, timid, retiring. It may raid the vegetable plot, but it does not attack man or man's domestic animals. Its little excursions to nibble carrots, lettuces, peas, are tiresome, but, like the misbehavior of children whom we nevertheless love, can be corrected by our own watchfulness. Like children, the rabbits in garden, field and hutch endear themselves to us by their innocent, happy preoccupation with their simple way of living. Small wonder that in the traditional nursery tales the rabbit is both the *enfant terrible* and the lovable character. Beatrix Potter and a hundred other authors have created the acceptable image of careless, cheerful, clever Rabbit. Those enchanting Little People, the gnomes, goblins, elves and pixies, have long rabbit-like ears. Uncle Remus's Brer Rabbit always wins in the battle of wits with Brer Fox; Baby-face triumphs once more over Long Nose.

Ronald M. Lockley

Getting a Hare's Goat

The man who encounters the hare
Will never get the better of him,
Except he lay down on ground
The weapon he bears in his hand
(Be it hunting-staff or bow),
And bless him with his elbow.
And with sincere devotion
Utter this one prayer
In praise of the hare –
Then will he better fare:
'The hare, the hare-kin,
Old Big-bum, Old Bouchart,
The hare-ling, the frisky one,
Old Turpin, the fast traveller,
The way-beater, the white-spotted one,
The lurker in ditches, the filthy beast,
Old Wimount, the coward,
The link-away, the nibbler,
The One it's bad luck to meet, the white-livered,
The scutter, the fellow in the dew,
The grass nibbler, Old Goibert,
The one who doesn't go straight home, the traitor,

The friendless one, the cat of the wood,
The starer with wide eyes, the cat that lurks in the broom,
The purblind one, the furze-cat,
The clumsy one, the blear-eyed one,
The wall-eyed one, the looker to the side,
And also the hedge-frisker,
The stag of the stubble, long-eared
The animal of the stubble, the springer,
The wild animal, the jumper,
The short animal, the lurker,
The swift-as-wind, the skulker,
The shagger, the squatter in the hedge,
The dew-beater, the dew hopper,
The sitter on its form, the hopper in the grass,
The fidgety-footed one, the sitter on the ground,
The light-foot, the sitter in the bracken,
The stag of the cabbages, the cropper of herbage,
The low creeper, the sitter-still,
The small-tailed one, the one who turns to the hills,
The get-up quickly,
The one who makes you shudder,
The white-bellied one,
The one that takes refuge with the lambs,
The numbskull, the food mumbler,
The niggard, the flincher,
The one who makes people flee, the covenant-breaker,

The snuffler, the cropped head
(His chief name is Scoundrel),
The stag with the leathery hornes,
The animal that dwells in the corn,
The animal that all men scorn,
The animal that no one dare name.'
When you have said all this,
Then is the hare's strength put down,
Then you might go out
East, west, north and south,
Wherever a man will –
A man that has any skill.
And now, good day to you, Sir Hare!
God let you in such wise fare
As will bring you to me dead,
Either in onion broth or just in bread!

Anonymous

Appendix

Rabbit Reference

- **bunny:** pet name
- **bunny:** dupe or dolt; habitually perplexed person
- **bunny:** to talk or chat excessively
- **bunny cat:** Abyssinian cat; bobtail cat
- **bunny-grub:** green vegetables
- **bunny hop:** short leap
- **bunny hug:** dance popular about 1910
- **bunnymouth:** snapdragon

- **hare:** to run fast
- **hare:** constellation Lepus
- **hare:** passenger without ticket (British)
- **hare and hounds:** game in which players as hares are followed by players as hounds
- **harebell:** perennial herb with blue flowers; wood hyacinth
- **harebottle:** knapweed
- **hare-brained:** foolish, flighty, giddy

- **harebur:** burdock
- **hare ears:** showing fear and suspicion
- **hare-eyed:** having eyes timidly alert
- **hare-finder:** leader in rabbit-hunting expedition
- **hare-foot:** long, narrow foot; rabbit-foot clover
- **hare foot:** showing agility and speed
- **harehearted:** timorous
- **harehound:** one used to hunt hares
- **hare kangaroo:** small Australian kangaroo resembling hare
- **harelip:** congenital fissure in upper lip; being harelipped
- **harelipped bat:** large tropical American fish-eating bat
- **harelip sucker:** cutlip
- **hare-sleep:** feigned sleep
- **hare tracks:** showing fleetness or swiftness
- **hare's-bane:** wolf's bane
- **hare's-meat:** wood-sorrel

- *hare's-parsley:* European herb
- *rabbit:* a cheap fur
- *rabbit:* contemptible person; a novice
- *rabbit:* new-born babe
- *rabbit:* salad, composed of greens
- *rabbit:* sort of wooden drinking vessel
- *rabbit and pork:* to talk or chat
- *rabbit ball:* baseball
- *rabbit-eared:* like a rabbit's ears
- *rabbit-ear faucet:* self-closing faucet
- *rabbit ears:* showing sensitivity to criticism; portable TV antenna
- *rabbit fish:* any of several kinds resembling rabbit
- *rabbit flower (also rabbit-ear):* toad-flax; purple foxglove
- *rabbit food:* vegetable salad; any kind of greens
- *rabbit-foot:* to move quickly; to escape from prison
- *rabbit-foot grass:* European clover or rabbit's foot, a weedy grass
- *rabbit hawk:* red-tailed hawk
- *rabbit hutch:* coop in which rabbits are bred
- *rabbit louse:* common louse on rabbits
- *rabbit-meat:* red archangel
- *rabbit moth:* moth affecting southern oranges
- *rabbitmouth:* rabbitmouth sucker
- *rabbit-mouthed:* hare-lipped
- *rabbit-o:* seller of rabbits on streets
- *rabbit pea:* catgut
- *rabbit-pie:* harlot
- *rappit-pie shifter:* policeman
- *rabbit punch (also rabbiter):* sharp blow to back of head
- *rabbit rat:* small rodent or bandicoot
- *rabbitroot:* wild sarsaparilla
- *rabbitry:* group of hutches for rabbits
- *rabbits:* contraband or smuggled goods; customs officer
- *rabbit's-ear cabbage:* Canadian weed

- *rabbit's foot:* hind leg of rabbit used as talisman for good luck
- *rabbit's foot clover:* rabbit-foot clover
- *rabbit's-foot fern:* serpent fern
- *rabbit-skin:* parchment for certificate or diploma
- *rabbit squirrel:* large South American rodent
- *rabbit stick or club:* boomerang
- *rabbit-sucker:* young spendthrift
- *rabbit-tail grass:* hare's-tail grass
- *rabbit thorn:* rough and thorny shrub
- *rabbit tick:* common tick
- *rabbit tobacco:* balsamweed
- *rabbit vine:* groundnut
- *rabbit warren:* place to keep rabbits; crowded tenement house
- *rabbit, Welsh (also Welsh rarebit):* melted cheese and toast
- *rabbitweed:* stiff woody herb
- *rabbitwood:* shrub parasitic on hemlocks
- *rabbity:* like or resembling rabbit

Rabbit Sayings

- Crazy as a March hare
- Cute as a bunny
- Funny as a bunny
- Harried as a rabbit
- Jumps like a rabbit
- Like sending carrots by a rabbit
- Mad as a March hare
- Multiply like rabbits
- Quicker than a rabbit to his hole
- Runs like a rabbit
- Swift as a hare
- Timid as a hare
- Make a hare of: to make ridiculous
- Make rabbits: to follow a hobby
- Buy the rabbit or rabbits: to have worst of bargain
- Run the rabbit: to convey liquor from a public-house
- Get one's rabbit-skin: to get college bachelor's degree
- Swallow a hare: to get very drunk
- Seek a hare in a hen's nest: to try to do the impossible
- Go rabbit-hunting or cony-catching with a dead ferret: unsuitable or useless means
- Kiss the hare's foot: to be late. Cf. Get the hare's foot to lick: to get little or nothing
- It's rabbits out of the woods: windfall or sheer profit
- Set the hare's head against the goose giblets: stingy or unfair exchange
- Like a fat and lean rabbit: responding promptly to food after being lean for twenty-four hours